D0188062

YOUR BODY YOUR HEALTH

THE
BLOOD
& IMMUNE
SYSTEM

YOUR BODY YOUR HEALTH

THE
BLOOD
& IMMUNE
SYSTEM

Reader's Digest

The Reader's Digest Association Limited

London New York Sydney Montreal

The Blood and Immune System

was created and produced by
Carroll & Brown Limited
20 Lonsdale Road
London NW6 6RD
for Reader's Digest, London

First English Edition Copyright © 2002
The Reader's Digest Association Limited
11 Westferry Circus
Canary Wharf
London E14 4HE
www.readersdigest.co.uk

Copyright © 2002 The Reader's Digest
Association Far East Limited
Philippines copyright © 2002 The Reader's
Digest Association Far East Limited

All rights reserved.
No part of this book may be reproduced, stored
in a retrieval system or transmitted in any form
or by any means, electronic, electrostatic,
magnetic tape, mechanical, photocopying,
recording or otherwise, without permission in
writing from the publishers.

® Reader's Digest, The Digest and the
Pegasus logo are registered trademarks of
The Reader's Digest Association Inc. of
Pleasantville, New York, USA.

ISBN 0 276 42703 3

Reproduced by Colourscan, Singapore
Printed and bound by Printer Industria
Gráfica S. A., Barcelona

**The information in this book is for
reference only; it is not intended as a
substitute for a doctor's diagnosis and
care. The editors urge anyone with
continuing medical problems or
symptoms to consult a doctor.**

Managing editor
Anne Yelland

Managing art editor
Anne Fisher

Editors
Judy Fovargue, Marianne Canty, Anna Southgate

Art editors
Maxine Lea, Vimit Punater

Design assistants
Justin Ford, Jim Cheatle

Series medical consultant
Dr Lesley Hickin, MB BS, BSc, DRCOG, MRCGP, General Practitioner

Specialist immunology consultant
Dr Matthew Helbert, MBChB, MRCP, MRCPath, PhD, Consultant Immunologist,
Manchester Royal Infirmary

CONTRIBUTORS

Dr Wynnie Chan, BSc, PhD, Public Health Nutritionist

Chrissie Gallagher-Mundy, BA (Hons), Fitness Writer,
Director, London Academy of Personal Fitness

Katy Glynne, BSc, MRPharmS, Dip Pharmacy Practice,
Clinical Services Manager, Charing Cross Hospital, London,
Clinical Lecturer, The School of Pharmacy, University of London

Dr Matthew Helbert

Dr Martin L. Hibberd, PhD, Lecturer in Infectious Diseases,
Imperial College Faculty of Medicine, Department of Paediatrics, St Mary's Hospital, London

Joel Levy, BSc, MA, Medical Writer

Mr Gareth Page, BSc, MSc, Laboratory Manager, Clinical Transplantation Laboratory,
Guy's and St Thomas' Hospitals NHS Trust, London
Training Coordinator for the British Society for Histocompatibility and Immunogenics (BSHI)

Jo Robinson, National Development and Training Officer,
Terrence Higgins Trust

For Reader's Digest
Series Editor Christine Noble
Art Editor Julie Bennett
Editorial Assistant Lucy Murray
Reader's Digest General Books
Editorial Director Cortina Butler
Art Director Nick Clark

The Blood and Immune System

Awareness of health issues and expectations of medicine are greater today than ever before. A long and healthy life has come to be looked on as not so much a matter of luck but as almost a right. However, as our knowledge of health and the causes of disease has grown, it has become increasingly clear that health is something that we can all influence, for better or worse, through choices we make in our lives. *Your Body Your Health* is designed to help you make the right choices to make the most of your health potential. Each volume in the series focuses on a different physiological system of the body, explaining what it does and how it works. There is a wealth of advice and health tips on diet, exercise and lifestyle factors, as well as the health checks you can expect throughout life. You will find out what can go wrong and what can be done about it, and learn from people's real-life experiences of diagnosis and treatment. Finally, there is a detailed A to Z index of the major conditions which can affect the system. The series builds into a complete user's manual for the care and maintenance of the entire body.

This volume on the blood and immune system looks at how your body protects itself. It reveals how blood is formed and the highly specialised functions of its component cell types, from iron-rich red blood cells that carry oxygen, to killer cells that conquer and neutralise invaders. You will discover the vital role of lymph fluid in guarding against infection, and what goes on in the lymphatic system when an enemy is detected. The book describes what happens when people give blood, and what has been done to make sure the blood donation system is safe for both donors and recipients. You will find out how to ensure you get the nutrients your blood and immune system needs, why too much exercise can be harmful, and how vaccination to promote immunity to disease has transformed health prospects worldwide. Finally, the book discusses what can go wrong with the blood and immune system and the range of diagnostic and treatment options available today, including state-of-the-art techniques such as stem cell therapy.

Contents

1

How your blood and immune system works

2

Healthy systems for life

TAKE CHARGE OF YOUR HEALTH

EATING FOR BLOOD AND IMMUNE HEALTH

EXERCISING FOR CIRCULATORY HEALTH

PROTECTING YOURSELF

3

What happens when things go wrong

The life story of the blood and immune system

The ancients believed that blood contained the life force, the supernatural energy that animated all living things. From the time of the great Greek and Roman physicians it was believed that there were several fundamental energies at work in the body and that blood was the medium through which these energies moved.

According to the medical system of the Roman physician Galen, followed by every doctor in Europe until the 17th century, blood delivered natural spirits (the 'spark of life') and vital spirits (which provided the power of movement) to all parts of the body.

Several centuries of scientific endeavour have arrived at very similar conclusions, with the words 'nutrients' and 'oxygen' substituted for natural and vital spirits. Blood distributes nutrients around the body, making life possible, and, in particular, delivers oxygen to the muscles, where it is used to provide the energy for movement. But our modern understanding, although it confirms ancient wisdom in some respects, is both more detailed and more profound. We now know that blood is part of a complex system of cells and tissues with closely linked origins and functions, which plays an essential role in maintaining the health and well-being of every cell in your body.

VERSATILE BLOOD

Not all living things have blood — microorganisms, plants and even simple animals like sponges make do without. But evolving a liquid medium such as blood for the transport of gases and nutrients was essential if animals were to evolve any further than the level of sponges — to become large, complex and active. Blood allows different parts of the body, sometimes separated by considerable distances — the head and tail of a blue whale may be more than 30 metres (100 feet) apart — to perform specialised tasks without having to worry about securing their own supplies of nutrients. Its efficiency in delivering oxygen allows animals to maintain a high activity rate, and its ability to reach every tissue makes it an essential component in the

There are around 50 billion white cells in your bloodstream, whose function is to protect you from infection.

process of homeostastis that maintains constant conditions within the body, ironing out fluctuations that could threaten to disrupt the functioning of the whole. Using a fluid medium for nutrient transportation introduces the risk of leaks, but blood has evolved its own solution to the problem of bleeding. It carries with it a sophisticated system for plugging gaps and stopping leaks.

ACTIVE DEFENCE

However, your body needs more protection than simply plugging leaks in the blood supply. Partly thanks to the success of blood your body is an attractive target for many kinds of organism, such as bacteria, viruses and parasites, which seek to exploit your body's resources. This can upset the delicate balance of internal conditions that your body requires. To protect you against attack you need robust and effective safeguards. But your defence system must also have other properties, if it is not to do more harm than good.

For instance, a defence system that simply attacks at will would quickly destroy any cells it encounters, including friendly cells belonging to your own body (known as 'self').

So a defence system must be selective: it must know how to tell the difference between invaders ('non-self' organisms) and friendly cells, and it must be able to target its response accordingly. To make matters even more complicated, the distinction between self and non-self is not always clear, as invaders use cunning stratagems to try to foil your defences. Some hide inside your own cells, while others seek to change their external appearance faster than your defences can respond.

HEALTHY COMPETITION

Power, selectivity and sophistication are thus the requirements for a defence system – and an effective immune system meets all of them. Competition with microorganisms has

Size does not matter
A constant supply of blood – and therefore oxygen – means that the different body parts of even the largest creatures are able to function as a whole, and in tandem with one another.

led to an evolutionary arms race. The result is an immune system equipped with an astonishingly sophisticated army of cells and proteins that interact, stimulate and regulate each other in ways we are only just beginning to understand. Some of these cells patrol the bloodstream, some the tissues of the body. Others make their home in a system of vessels and nodes known as the lymphatic system, which filters fluids from the tissues before it returns them to the bloodstream. Your blood, your lymphatic system, and the immune system whose components they make up, are collectively referred to as the haemolymphatic system.

HOW THE BLOOD AND IMMUNE SYSTEM DEVELOP

The first blood cells appear in the primitive circulatory system of a developing embryo just three weeks after fertilisation, but they are created outside the actual embryo – in a yolk sac, a developmental reminder of our shared ancestry with birds and reptiles. These blood cells derive from a type of cell in the yolk sac called an embryonic blood cell (EBC). EBCs are a type of stem cell – a cell whose destiny is not fixed, but which can give rise to several different lineages of daughter cell.

As soon as they appear in the embryo the EBCs start to divide, producing more of their kind and also the first oxygen-carrying red blood cells, which make up the bulk of blood. They also produce white blood cells – immune system cells that provide the embryo with its first, rudimentary defences against infection. About six weeks after fertilisation, EBCs migrate through the primitive circulatory system to the developing liver and spleen,

Early beginnings
Embryonic blood cells are evident as early as three weeks into the life of a developing embryo.

IMMUNITY FOR LIFE

The immune system is fully developed from early infancy, and offers protection against hostile viruses, bacteria and parasites. Although its strength depends primarily on genetic inheritance, there are lifestyle choices you can make to help maintain its function and efficiency.

where they take up residence and set to work producing billions of red blood cells.

As new blood cells flood into the developing baby's circulation, its immune system is also developing and maturing. The thymus is a lymphatic organ that helps to nurture and train immune cells, so that they can tell self from non-self. It first appears during the fourth week of pregnancy and slowly enlarges. White blood cells from the yolk sac, and later the liver and spleen, migrate into the thymus and begin their training. By week 17 of pregnancy the first fully trained and operational white blood cells emerge and begin to patrol the body, although their functions are still suppressed – up until birth, a developing baby will continue to depend primarily on its mother to protect it against invaders.

Blood accounts for about 7 per cent of your body weight.
Therefore, on average, men have 5–6 litres (9–11 pints) of blood,
and women have 4–5 litres (7–9 pints).

The Guthrie blood test
Blood samples are taken from newborn babies by pricking the relatively insensitive skin on the heel. The blood sample is tested for phenylketonuria, a rare genetic disorder.

NEWBORN

CHILDHOOD

TEENAGE

Keeping disease at bay
From infancy through adulthood, medical developments have allowed us to boost our immune system's responses through vaccination.

Fitness first
Physical and mental health are now known to effect the immune system, making it sensible to exercise regularly from an early age.

READY FOR ACTION

After about six months, EBCs in the bone marrow – the soft, gel-like central core of each bone – take over from those in the liver and spleen. At first practically every bone in the developing fetus's body is involved in generating blood cells, a process called haemopoiesis, but after birth this function is concentrated in a few key bones, including the vertebrae, ribs and pelvis. This still leaves the growing infant with more than enough blood-producing capacity – under normal circumstances a child produces more than 10 billion new blood cells every day (mostly to replace existing ones).

The thymus continues to grow throughout pregnancy, until, at birth, it is much larger in relative terms than it ever will be again. This equips the newborn to produce lots of functional white blood cells rapidly, as its own immune system takes over from its mother's. However, there is a maternal parting gift in the form of antibodies – immune system proteins that help to target and destroy threatening germs. Many proteins are too large to cross the placental barrier between the maternal and fetal blood, but the mother manufactures an antibody called IgG which is actively pumped across. Another brand of antibodies, called IgA, are passed by the mother in her breast milk and taken up by the infant through the gut. Despite this lingering immune 'umbrella' from its mother, a young infant remains vulnerable for the first few weeks while its own immune system gets up to speed, developing some robust defences that will provide protection, themselves reaching full maturity at about age five. Only

You are what you eat
Vitamins K and B$_{12}$ are essential for your blood clotting system and the production of new blood cells respectively.

A question of age
The immune system weakens as we grow older. Fewer cells are produced, by the thymus gland, thus increasing our risk of infection when exposed to bacteria and viruses.

ADULT

ELDERLY

in later years does the immune system begin to weaken. The thymus very slowly degenerates, fewer new immune system cells are produced to replace ones that have died, and exposure to threats produces a steadily weaker immune response. This process happens at different rates for different people – the strength of your immune system is partly determined by your genetic inheritance, but day-to-day lifestyle can be important too.

HAEMOLYMPHATIC HEALTH TIPS

Your diet affects both the readiness of your white blood cells to fight infection, and the health of your red blood cells and the other blood components. You depend on essential vitamins such as B$_{12}$, found in meats and dairy products, to help you manufacture new blood cells, while your blood clotting system won't work properly if you don't eat enough vitamin K (found in cabbage, spinach and other green leafy vegetables, as well as cereals and soya).

Exercise has been shown to boost the immune system, and doctors are increasingly coming to realise that mental health can be a powerful influence. Studies show that loneliness and boredom depress the immune system, while laughter, being surrounded by loved ones and even the company of pets can have a direct beneficial effect on the activity of your white blood cells.

As the blood and immune system form the basis of resistance to disease and illness of all kinds, it's important to look after them through a healthy lifestyle – and to make full use of today's medical technology. Vaccination programmes such as those against polio and smallpox have given medicine some of its greatest success stories, but recent scares about the safety of some routine childhood vaccines have highlighted the need for increased awareness about issues of blood and immune health. Overwhelming medical opinion is that any risk posed by the vaccinations is far outweighed by the risks of not having them.

A person who lives to be over 70 has a
95 per cent of needing blood or blood products
at some point in their life.

FRIENDLY FIRE

Evidence is emerging from many different branches of medical research that the immune system itself may be responsible for some of the most serious illnesses affecting the developed world — illnesses that are increasingly common. In some of these illnesses, such as allergies and arthritis, the role of a malfunctioning immune system has been known for many years. Recent discoveries, however, have also suggested that modern plagues such as depression and atherosclerosis may be linked to an abnormal immune response. For example, according to researchers at the French national medical research agency, INSERM, signalling chemicals used by the immune system to increase immune activity are also linked to those governing mood in the brain.

Such findings suggest that the solutions to some of our biggest problems today might be held by the immune system itself. For instance, it is possible that, in future, a bout of depression will be treated by an immunologist, rather than a psychiatrist.

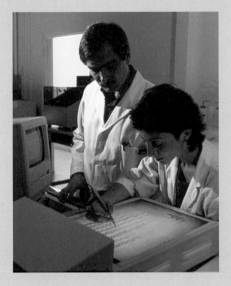

Hope for the future
Scientists around the world are trying to develop a vaccine for AIDS. HIV (below) — the virus which may lead to AIDS — attacks the body's cells' DNA. Scientists examine damaged DNA sequences (above) to further their knowledge of how HIV and DNA interact.

THE SHAPE OF THINGS TO COME

Stimulating the immune system through vaccination has been a huge success. Up until the 1970s, millions of people had died of smallpox: this disease has now been eradicated through global vaccination. As our understanding of the haemolymphatic system advances, so does the potential for radical new treatments. Some of these are already at the testing stage — around the world new vaccines for AIDS and tuberculosis are raising hopes that these plagues could at last be brought under control. Synthetic blood is a long-cherished dream of the medical profession — a successful version could solve the problem of blood shortages.

But the real revolutions in haemolymphatic medicine are some way off, because not until scientists gain a better understanding of the web of interactions between the elements of blood and the immune system will they be able to manipulate and control them. Once we have this understanding, new treatments for mankind's major afflictions could be produced. White blood cells could be engineered to overcome antibiotic-resistant microorganisms; the cells of transplanted organs could be engineered to be a perfect match for the recipient; allergies could be cured; and ageing immune systems could be rejuvenated. This is not fiction, it is based on fact, and on the extraordinary abilities of the blood and immune system.

1

How your blood and immune system works

Your amazing blood and immune system

The remarkable fluid that sustains and nourishes your body also protects it against dangers from inside and out. Working in conjunction with the lymphatic system, blood provides a highly efficient defence system that fights off a multitude of invaders to keep you in good health.

THE FUNCTIONS OF THE BLOOD

The cells of your body require a constant supply of oxygen and nutrients, and generate waste products that can be toxic if they build up. Oxygen, nutrients and waste products can all move short distances on their own via the process of diffusion, but your body is too big for such a short-range process to meet the needs of your cells. You need a specialised fluid medium that can perform these essential tasks – this is the blood that flows through your circulatory system.

Functions of the blood include:

- Transport – of oxygen and carbon dioxide to and from the lungs; of nutrients from the digestive system; of waste products to the kidneys and liver; and of hormones and enzymes to their target tissues.

- Defence and clotting to neutralise threats and seal off injuries.
- Regulation of pH and temperature – your blood dilutes acid produced by working muscles and redistributes heat evenly around the body.

TO PROTECT AND SIEVE

Your blood is part of a highly evolved immune system that helps to protect the body against pathogens (a pathogen is anything that threatens your body on a cellular level, such as a bacterium, virus or poison) and filters out dead or diseased cells. Another component of the immune system is the lymphatic system, a set of vessels and structures that deals with a fluid called lymph and immune system cells called lymphocytes.

The lymphatic system *is comprised of vessels that transport lymph fluid and many immune cells. They follow the paths of your body's arteries and veins – see pages 28–29 for more details.*

The thymus *helps to 'train' cells of your immune system to tell the difference between 'friendly cells' and pathogens. Pages 32–33 describe how.*

The blood circulatory system *carries oxygenated blood from the heart and lungs along arteries to all the tissues of the body, and then returns the deoxygenated blood back to the heart and lungs via the veins. Find out more about the composition of this life-giving fluid on pages 18–19.*

Target and destroy

Antibodies are proteins produced by cells of the immune system that are specialised to recognise and lock on to pathogens, aiding and amplifying the immune response. See pages 36–37 for more.

Small soldiers

Circulating in your bloodstream and lymphatic system is an army of immune cells known as white blood cells. The many varieties of white blood cell, and their functions, are described on pages 22–23 and 28–29.

The spleen is the largest lymphatic organ – it helps to filter the blood and stores blood components for emergencies. Find out more on pages 34–35.

Lymph nodes – found at intervals along the lymph vessels – filter lymph and provide a base for lymphocytes. See pages 30–31.

Blood from bone

Blood is produced in bone marrow, and the pelvis is one of the most prolific contributors. To find out more see pages 26–27.

Emergency repairs

If your circulatory system springs a leak, it is vital to repair it as quickly as possible. Discover how your blood repairs punctures and wounds on pages 24–25.

Workhorses

Red blood cells, also known as erythrocytes, are the workhorses of the circulation, carrying oxygen to cells and picking up waste carbon dioxide in return. They give blood its characteristic colour. Pages 20–21 examine red blood cells in detail.

Composition of the blood

*The blood in your body may look like a liquid but it is
actually a suspension of particles in a liquid – that is,
billions of cells floating in a watery fluid rich in proteins
and nutrients.*

The walls of an artery *are cut away here
to show how they consist of a series of elastic
and muscular layers. These help to push
blood forward along the artery, so that blood
is carried swiftly away from the heart and
around the body.*

BLOOD PLASMA – THICKER THAN WATER

A straw-coloured fluid called plasma makes up 55 per cent of
the volume of blood. Plasma is mostly water – about 92 per cent
of it – but carries dissolved within it substances that include:

- Nutrients that the cells of your body (including
  those in the bloodstream) need for survival,
  growth and function. These include glucose
  and amino acids.
- Waste products that are being
  transported from the cells that made
  them to the body's filtration and
  disposal organs (the liver
  and kidneys).
- Ions including sodium,
  potassium, calcium and
  magnesium. Some of these
  are minerals needed by cells,
  but in general they are there
  to maintain the
  concentration of blood at
  the correct level, and to
  maintain the balance of
  other body fluids.
- Proteins, including: albumins,
  which again help to maintain
  the concentration of the blood
  and also transport fats (which are
  normally insoluble in water);
  globulins, which have several roles,
  including defence and transport of
  hormones; and fibrinogen, which is the
  inactive form of fibrin. Fibrin is a long, sticky,
  insoluble protein that helps to coagulate the blood
  and form blood clots.

BLOOD CELLS

The 45 per cent of blood that is not plasma is composed of a
mixture of cells and cell fragments collectively known as blood
cells. There are three main types: red blood cells, white blood
cells and platelets.

AN EVER-CHANGING STREAM

The mix of red blood cells, white blood cells and
platelets in the bloodstream is constantly
changing as cells move in and out of tissues, old
cells die and new ones replace them. Blood loss
from injury will temporarily decrease the number
of cells, while spending time at a higher altitude
will increase the number, as more red blood cells
are made to compensate for the lower oxygen
levels at a high altitude. By training at high
altitude, athletes use this phenomenon to boost
the oxygen-carrying powers of their blood.

A white blood cell
The white blood cell in this coloured transmission electron micrograph (TEM) is a plasma cell – a B lymphocyte in its mature, activated form; the cell's nucleus is shown as dark red. Plasma cells produce antibodies.

Platelets *are not really cells, but small packets of cytoplasm (the gel-like substance inside a cell) enclosed by a membrane. There is roughly one platelet for every 15 red blood cells.*

Plasma *is a sticky, viscous fluid because of the various nutrients, proteins and other substances that are dissolved within it.*

Red blood cells *account for more than 99 per cent of all blood cells.*

White blood cells *are very much less numerous than red blood cells – there is roughly one white blood cell for every 700 red blood cells. They come in several different shapes and sizes.*

Red blood cells

The main component of blood, the red blood cell is both unusually shaped and highly specialised. It has a simple structure that is tough and durable enough to travel hundreds of kilometres and yet flexible enough to bend double.

A UNIQUE PROFILE

Red blood cells – also called erythrocytes – lack internal structures that are vital to almost every other cell in the body. A red blood cell has no mitochondria, the oxygen-burning, energy-producing structures that act as cellular generators, and no nucleus – the cellular control centre that contains DNA and normally directs a cell's operations, in particular the manufacture of proteins. These structures are present when a red blood cell is born, but are lost as it matures.

Instead of mitochondria and nuclei, red blood cells are packed with an oxygen-carrying protein called haemoglobin – up to a third of a red blood cell's cytoplasm is pure haemoglobin. Haemoglobin is the medium by which oxygen is transported throughout the body. Not having any mitochondria helps the red blood cell to avoid 'stealing' its own cargo of oxygen, while the lack of a nucleus cuts down the cell's energy requirements as it precludes the manufacture of proteins. Red blood cells get all the energy they need from glucose in the plasma around them.

A third of the total number of cells in the human body are red blood cells. Thus, an average man has around 75 trillion red cells in the bloodstream and an average woman has about 60 trillion red cells.

BLOOD TYPES

There are four blood types: O, A, B and AB, any of which may be Rhesus positive or Rhesus negative (see page 58). The blood type of any individual is determined by their red blood cells. The reasoning behind this is as follows:

1 All the cells in your body are equipped with surface molecules that identify them as 'self' or 'foreign', enabling the cells of your body to recognise one another.
2 On red blood cells these molecules are known as 'agglutinins', and there are more than 50 different types.
3 The most important types are the A, B and Rhesus agglutinins, the presence or absence of which determine your blood type. For instance, AB+ denotes someone whose red blood cells have all three of these agglutinins, while O– indicates that none of them are present.

An average red blood cell lives for
120 days, during which time it
travels some 500km/300 miles,
on its non-stop journey round
and round the body.

Like a magnet
*The large complex proteins that make
up haemoglobin are each composed
of four sub-chains, each containing
a central molecule of 'haem' – an
iron-containing complex that can
pick up, carry and drop oxygen
molecules. It is the presence of this
iron/oxygen combination that gives
haemoglobin, and therefore your blood,
its distinctive colour.*

VITAL STATISTICS
- Red blood cells are disc-like cells about 0.008mm wide.
- They are 0.0026mm thick around the edges but only 0.0008mm thick in the centre, giving them a distinctive doughnut shape. This means they can pile up on top of one another like dinner plates, to give stacks called 'rouleaux', allowing many of them to pass through a vessel only fractionally wider than a single red blood cell without jamming it up.
- The flattened shape of a red blood cell gives it a large surface area, increasing its capacity for gaseous exchange – to deliver life-giving oxygen to the body's cells and exchange it for their waste product of carbon dioxide. The total surface area of all the red blood cells in an average adult is estimated at around 3800 square metres – enough to cover four tennis courts.
- Red blood calls are extremely flexible, allowing them to bend and squeeze through narrow spaces, so that they can carry their load of oxygen into every nook and cranny of the body.

White blood cells

Circulating in your blood and scattered through all the tissues of your body is an army of defensive cells, collectively known as white blood cells or leucocytes. Like soldiers in an army they are trained to perform different roles, and to work in concert to defeat the enemy.

SMALL SOLDIERS

White blood cells, or leucocytes, derive their name from their colourless appearance under a microscope, when compared with red blood cells. They perform a variety of vital roles in the immune system. Some, such as neutrophils, are specialised to recognise and identify pathogens, and then relay this information to others, which in turn are specialised to attack and destroy the pathogens. Some – notably neutrophils – spend most of their time circulating in the bloodstream, while others – such as mast cells – spend their time in the tissues of the body (known as peripheral tissues). Most move between the bloodstream and the tissues.

The types of white blood cells known as lymphocytes spend much of their time in the lymphatic system (see pages 28–29).

Monocytes
Making up 5–10 per cent of circulating white blood cells, monocytes are large phagocytic cells programmed to roam peripheral tissues looking for pathogens. They are antigen-presenting cells (APCs): when they find a pathogen they digest it and express one of its antigens on their own surface, activating other white blood cells to hunt for that specific antigen. A pathogen such as a virus could present dozens of potential antigens, each offering a potential route of attack for the immune system.

Monocyte

Eosinophils
Making up only 2–4 per cent of the circulating white blood cell population, eosinophils mostly patrol peripheral tissues. They are able to attack the surface of pathogens too big to be eaten by neutrophils.

Eosinophil

Glossary

Antibody *A protein molecule produced by a lymphocyte in response to the presence of a particular antigen; it attacks the antigen and renders it harmless.*

Antigen *A molecule – of poison, for example, or of a bacterial cell wall – that evokes an immune response. A pathogen such as a virus could present dozens of potential antigens.*

Erythrocyte *A red blood cell.*

Leucocyte *A white blood cell.*

Lymphocyte *A variety of white blood cell that is mostly found in the lymphatic system.*

Pathogen *Anything that threatens the body on a cellular level, such as a bacterium, virus, molecule of poison or a cancerous cell.*

Phagocyte *A cell that consumes and breaks down other cells or pathogens.*

Neutrophils

*The most common type of white blood cell found in the
bloodstream, neutrophils are short-lived, surviving for only 12 hours.
They are highly mobile, aggressive phagocytes that consume other
cells or pathogens. They are the first white blood cells to appear at
the site of an injury, where they consume germs that may have got
into the wound, and then themselves break down and release
chemicals that attract other immune cells.*

Neutrophil

Mast cell

Mast cells

*Permanently anchored in peripheral
tissue, mast cells are filled with
granules of histamine. They are largely
responsible for the allergic response.*

Basophils

*Usually found in peripheral tissues,
these are filled with granules of
histamine, a substance that triggers
inflammation and is involved in the
allergic response. They release their
granules when they encounter
damaged tissue.*

23

Platelets and clotting

With up to 5 or 6 litres (9 to 11 pints) of blood pumping round your system at high pressure, the danger posed by a leak of any sort is considerable. Platelets and proteins called clotting factors provide your blood with a system of 'leak-control'.

HOW A BLOOD CLOT FORMS

When a blood vessel wall becomes damaged and a tear develops, millions of platelets come together to form a platelet plug, enmeshed in a skeleton of fibrin fibres, that is attached to the sides of the tear. This process is triggered when a tear in a blood vessel wall exposes the collagen fibres inside it. Receptors on the surface of passing platelets bind to the exposed collagen fibres. The platelets become more crinkly to increase their surface area and stickiness. At the same time, they release signalling chemicals that attract other platelets and trigger substances called clotting factors.

These clotting factors activate one another in a series, culminating in the production of fibrin. Platelets and strands of fibrin combine into a clump that plugs the gap in the blood vessel wall. The platelets in the plug contain protein filaments like those found in muscles. After a platelet plug has formed, these filaments contract, shrinking the plug and drawing the sides of tear closer together. Immune system cells move in beneath the clot to clear away invading pathogens.

There are about 2 trillion platelets in the blood plus half that number again in reserve in the spleen. A platelet lives 10 days, so each day you lose and replace over 200 billion.

Platelets *hurry to the scene of the damage. In their inactivated state in the bloodstream, platelets are shaped like flattened discs. On activation (that is, when forming a clot) they change shape to become crinkly. This increases their adhesive qualities and also the surface area available for making contact with and binding to other platelets.*

CLOTTING FACTORS

- Clotting factors are the substances that activate and control the conversion of soluble fibrinogen in the blood into insoluble fibrin, molecules of which stick together to give a fibrous framework for clot formation.
- There are 14 clotting factors, or coagulation proteins, which interact in a specific sequence to generate thrombin, the enzyme that converts fibrinogen into fibrin.
- Each factor activates the next factor in sequence. This series of steps helps to produce a 'cascade' effect, so that one molecule of factor IX (one of the sequence starting points) can eventually generate up to 200 million molecules of fibrin. The step sequence is also a safeguard against the potential danger of the clotting process forming unwanted clots that can cause strokes and heart attacks.

As red blood cells *cascade from a tear in the blood vessel wall, exposed collagen fibres in the wall attract passing platelets, triggering the clotting process.*

Fibrin *is a strong, filament-like molecule that forms the framework of a clot, meshing together platelets and red blood cells. Until required, fibrin is held in the blood as soluble fibrinogen. Clotting factors stimulate its conversion into insoluble fibrin.*

The blood vessel wall *includes a thick layer of a fibrous protein called collagen. If the vessel wall is torn, these collagen fibres attract passing platelets.*

Platelets *are tiny membrane-enclosed packets of cytoplasm, no more than 0.003mm wide. They bind with strands of fibrin to form a clot. Once the clot has formed, protein filaments in the platelets contract to pull the sides of the tear together.*

Bone marrow – where blood comes from

Blood cells have a higher rate of turnover than practically any other tissue in the body, which makes the job of generating new blood cells a big one.

Red marrow bones
The bones involved in blood production on an everyday basis are highlighted here in pink – mainly the sternum, ribs, vertebrae and pelvis.

BLOOD FACTORY

All of the bones in your body have a spongy central core filled with a soft, pulpy tissue known as bone marrow, but only a few bones – primarily the vertebrae, sternum, ribs and pelvis – contain red marrow, which produces blood cells. In red marrow a network of blood vessels supply nutrients to and pick up new cells from clusters of blood-producing cells, called haemopoietic stem cells. Your bones contain 1–2 litres (1¾–3½ pints) of red marrow.

Red marrow is about half fat, whereas yellow marrow, found in most other bones, is almost all fat. However, yellow marrow does contain a small number of dormant haemopoietic cells, which can be reactivated if your body needs to generate large amounts of new blood cells – after blood loss from an injury, for example.

Blood cell production is controlled by hormones. A hormone called erythropoietin (EPO) – recently in the news because of its abuse by sports cheats – can convert yellow marrow into red, and increase the rate of red blood cell production tenfold.

BLOOD LINE

Haemopoietic stem cells are cells that, unlike most of the ones in your body, have not differentiated into particular cell types, and have the capacity to produce many different cell types. The most common haemopoietic cells are erythroblasts, which produce red blood cells. Other types give rise to different classes of white blood cell or to platelet-producing cells.

Vein

An osteon
– also known as a Haversian system – is one of the cylindrical units of which compact bone is made. At the centre of each osteon is a canal along which run blood vessels and nerves.

Red marrow produces around 3 million new red blood cells every second. Under stimulation by the hormone erythropoietin this can increase to an amazing 30 million a second.

26

Bone

Bone is the hard, dense, connective tissue that forms the skeleton of the body. It is chiefly composed of collagen fibres which confer resilience – and bone salts (chiefly calcium carbonate and calcium phosphate) which give the bones their rigidity. Bone marrow is contained in the central canal.

The blood vessels that snake through marrow are known as sinusoids. Red blood cells and platelets pass through gaps in the sinusoid lining.

Bone marrow is found in the medullary cavity, also known as the central canal, that runs down the centre of a bone. The cavity also contains spongy bone, blood vessels and nerves.

The blood-producing cells in the bone marrow gather in clusters known as haemopoietic clusters. These are supported by a framework of tissues made from fibroplast cells that run through the bone marrow.

Spongy bone within the medullary canal consists of a network of narrow bars of bony tissue called trabeculae. The interconnecting spaces within the trabeculae are filled with marrow.

Medullary cavity (central canal)

Compact or cortical bone – which lies between the periosteum and the medullary cavity – consists of many densely packed osteons.

The periosteum is the layer of dense connective tissue that covers the surface of a bone.

Artery

BLOOD-PRODUCING CELLS

Haemopoietic stem cells may be divided into several different types.

- Erythroblasts: red cell stem cells, which produce red cells.
- Myeloblasts: granulated cell stem cells, which give rise to white blood cells that can be subdivided into neutrophils, eosinophils and basophils.
- Lymphoblasts: lymphocyte stem cells that give rise to lymphocytes. Lymphoblasts migrate to lymphoid organs such as the spleen and thymus, where lymphocytes are produced and mature.

In addition, there are large cells in the bone marrow called megakaryocytes that produce platelets. A megakaryocyte produces a platelet by pinching off part of itself.

A macrophage at work
There is a macrophage at the centre of each haemopoietic cluster in the bone marrow. Macrophages help to clear away the debris of cell formation, such as nuclei lost from red blood cells as they mature. They also store iron, which they transfer to red blood cells. This coloured transmission electron micrograph (TEM) shows a macrophage engulfing a red blood cell.

The lymphatic system

Blood is not the only fluid circulating around your body. Complementing the circulatory system, and running parallel to much of it is a system of vessels and organs that transport lymph fluid and provide a home to many immune cells.

The right lymphatic duct *collects lymph from the right side of the body above the diaphragm and empties it into the right subclavian vein.*

Thymus

The thoracic duct *collects lymph from parts of the body below the diaphragm, and from the left side of the body above the diaphragm. This lymph drains into the left subclavian vein.*

Lymphatic organs *include the spleen, the thymus and the numerous lymph nodes. They house and train immune cells, such as B and T lymphocytes.*

The spleen *is the largest of the lymphatic organs.*

Lymph nodes *are strung in series along the more central lymph vessels. These nodes help to filter and clean the lymph before it passes back into the bloodstream.*

Lacteals *are large lymph vessels in the intestines that collect and transport fats.*

Lymphatic vessels *can be distinguished from blood vessels by their colour. Arteries are usually bright red, veins dark red and lymphatic vessels are pale golden in colour.*

Tiny blind-ended lymphatic capillaries *stretch into every part of the body's peripheral tissues to allow for the drainage of lymph fluid. These merge into larger lymph vessels that pass through numerous lymph nodes to clean the fluid prior to its re-entry into the blood.*

Up to 24 litres (14 pints) of lymph flow through your lymphatic system every day.

FLUID ASSETS

Tiny blood vessels called capillaries deliver blood to the peripheral tissues. As the capillaries narrow, the blood pressure inside them increases, squeezing plasma out through pores in the capillaries into the surrounding tissue. This fluid now becomes interstitial fluid. Most interstitial fluid rejoins the bloodstream by leaking back into the capillaries that drain the peripheral tissues. But the rest drains off by another route – the system of lymphatic vessels. This fluid is now called lymph and is similar to blood plasma, but generally has a lower concentration of proteins.

DRAINAGE SYSTEM

Your lymphatic system has two main functions.
- One is to nurture, train and maintain a population of immune cells. These are lymphocytes (types of white blood cells) that provide specific immunity – the main line of defence against bacterial and viral infections, and tumours. They spend much of the time in the lymphatic system but cross over into the bloodstream as required.
- The other is to return lymph to the bloodstream, so blood volume is maintained. This is achieved via a system of vessels, which starts with blind-ended lymphatic capillaries in the peripheral tissues. These merge to give larger vessels, which empty into two main lymphatic collecting ducts in the trunk of the body. The ducts return lymph to the bloodstream by draining into the subclavian veins. Unlike the vessels that transport blood, your lymphatic system is not a circulatory system – it is a drainage system.

One-way traffic
Your blood circulation is powered by the heart and the elastic, muscular artery walls. Your lymphatic system has neither of these. Pressure from the build-up of interstitial fluid, and energy from muscle movements, provide the driving force, and a system of valves keeps lymph flowing in the right direction.

Interstitial fluid *enters the lymph vessel from surrounding tissue. Once inside the vessel, the liquid is known as lymph.*

An open valve *allow lymph fluid to pass through.*

Direction of flow *of lymph fluid.*

Cross-section through a lymph vessel

A closed valve *prevents lymph fluid from flowing back the way it came.*

LYMPHOCYTES
- **Natural killer (NK) cells** *are lymphocytes that patrol for cancerous or virus-infected cells. When they find one they blast it with corrosive enzymes.*
- **B lymphocytes (B cells)** *turn into plasma cells – antibody producing factories – when activated. Each B cell is specialised to produce a specific antibody.*
- **T lymphocytes (T cells)** *come in three varieties:*
Cytotoxic T cells (CTL) *attack and kill pathogens that have been identified by the immune system – for example, ones tagged by antibodies – in the same way as do NK cells.*
Helper T cells (TH) *stimulate B lymphocytes to mature into plasma cells.*
Suppressor T cells (TS) *suppress B cell activity, helping to prevent immune responses from getting out of hand.*

TWO-PRONGED ATTACK
The army of white blood cells in your body provides you with two types of immune response:
- **Innate immunity** *Cells like neutrophils and NK cells patrol the body looking for pathogens. They don't need to be specifically primed – they will attack any suspicious antigens.*
- **Specific immunity** *T and B lymphocytes, together with antibodies, provide specific immunity. This type of immune response recognises and responds to specific antigens, and is able to give a bigger, faster and more effective response. It is also known as adaptive immunity, since B lymphocytes remember antigens they have encountered in the past and trigger an even bigger and more efficient immune response should these antigens ever reappear.*

Lymph nodes

If your body is a fortress and your immune system is an army guarding its walls, then lymph nodes are the barracks and watchtowers where that army makes its home and keeps watch for enemies – germs, cancerous cells, toxins – that threaten your health.

TOUR OF DUTY

After production and training in the bone marrow or thymus, lymphocytes enter the circulation to begin the fight against invaders and potential threats to the health. They circulate within lymph fluid and in the bloodstream and from here they cross over to one of several possible destinations composed of lymphoid tissue:

• The lymph nodes – small swellings found at intervals along the lymph vessels.

• Mucosa-associated lymphoid tissues (MALTs) such as the tonsils or the spleen, collectively termed the peripheral lymphoid organs.

Lymphocytes take up only temporary residence in these places, and are continually returning to the bloodstream to recirculate and take up another tour of duty elsewhere.

READY FOR ACTION

Lymph nodes and MALTs act as checkpoints and barracks – they filter lymph before it gets back into the bloodstream, and provide a base for a constantly but slowly changing population of lymphocytes. All types of lymphocyte live inside a node and are exposed to lymph as it drains through the passages of the node. If their specific target antigen comes through the lymph node, lymphocytes are activated and start to proliferate, signalling the start of the specific immune response.

Lymph nodes can be up to 25mm (1in) wide. There are more than 100 in your body.

A tough capsule
surrounds the node.

Section through a lymph node
The network of connective tissue that holds the lymph node together – made up of reticulin fibres – shows up as yellow in this coloured scanning electron micrograph (SEM). Amongst the fibres are white blood cells (seen here as green and yellow spheres) in various stages of development.

Inside a lymph node

Lymph nodes are small, oval organs distributed around the body, often in a chain following a lymph vessel. They vary in size from 1 to 25mm but all have a similar structure, comprising three main layers inside a tough outer capsule:

• An outer cortex where lymph flows in, and which houses mainly B cells. These are organised into primary follicles, which wait for antigens to flow past. When one does, the B cells are activated and form secondary follicles, proliferating and generating antibodies.

• A paracortex which contains antigen-presenting cells (APCs) and T cells. Phagocytes that also act as APCs line the channels through the lymph node.

• A medulla containing a mixture of B and T cells and phagocytes.

Lymph percolates through these layers and then out through an efferent lymphatic vessel.

Afferent lymph vessel

Interstitial fluid *enters the lymph vessel from surrounding tissue.*

Direction of flow *of lymph fluid.*

An afferent lymph vessel *along which lymph fluid enters the node.*

Afferent lymph vessel

The medulla *at the centre of the node contains a mixture of B cells and T cells.*

How lymph fluid travels through a lymph node *Several afferent lymph vessels bring lymph to the node, and feed through the capsule into the outer cortex. Lymph then percolates through the various layers of the node towards the efferent lymph vessel.*

Trabeculae *are the meshwork of fibrous partitions that provide the framework for the node.*

B cells in the outer cortex

T cells within the paracortex. *The paracortex also contains antigen-presenting cells (APCs).*

Artery

Vein

An efferent lymph vessel *carries lymph fluid away from the node.*

31

The thymus

T lymphocytes are highly specialised immune cells, trained to attack specific antigens, but how do they get that way? An organ called the thymus takes raw, unschooled lymphocytes and turns them into lean, mean fighting machines.

CENTRE STAGE

The thymus is relatively larger in a baby than in an adult, because it must work hard to provide the vulnerable child with a population of working lymphocytes. At puberty it reaches its full weight, around 20g (¾oz). From birth to puberty the thymus is deep red in colour because of its rich blood supply, but it becomes increasingly yellow with age as lymphoid tissue is gradually replaced with fibrous and fatty tissue. The degeneration of the thymus may be linked to a gradual decline in immune capability.

SUBJECT SELECTION

Before lymphocytes can provide specific immunity, they have to be trained to recognise specific antigens, and to distinguish between foreign antigens (non-self) and ones on the surface of the body's own cells (self). B lymphocytes (also called B cells) are trained in the bone marrow before being released into the bloodstream (although the 'B' refers not to the bone but to an organ in birds, called the Bursa of Fabricus, where these cells were first identified). T lymphocytes (also termed T cells), although initially produced in the bone marrow, are trained in the thymus.

The thymus *is a gland made of two oval-shaped lobes situated in the centre of the chest, usually just behind the sternum but in front of the heart and the major blood vessels. The two lobes are joined by connective tissue.*

Each lobe of the thymus *is divided into 2mm-wide lobules by fibrous partitions called septae.*

A fibrous capsule *covers the thymus and separates it into two lobes. Each lobe of the thymus has an outer cortex and an inner medulla.*

The capillaries that supply blood to the thymus *have unusually non-porous walls, to prevent antigens in the bloodstream from getting to the immature T cells and triggering them before they are fully trained. This is known as the blood-thymus barrier.*

Left lung

Left lobe

Right lobe of the thymus

Heart

Diaphragm

Vena cava

Aorta

Survival of the fittest – training camp for T cells
Immature lymphocytes travel from the bone marrow to the thymus via the bloodstream. As they journey through the thymus, they face a rigorous process that transforms the fittest into T lymphocytes.

1 *Immature T lymphocytes from the bone marrow enter the bloodstream to embark on their journey to the thymus.*

2 *The immature T lymphocytes enter a lobule of the thymus via the cortex, at which point they become known as thymocytes. As soon as they enter the cortex, thymocytes start to divide rapidly, but only 5 per cent make it through to the other side of the cortex – the rest (including those that might attack the body's own cells) are weeded out by nurse cells that live in the cortex.*

3 *As the surviving thymocytes move through the thymus they are exposed to a cocktail of hormones and growth factors, including alpha-thymosin, thymulin and thymopoietin. These help them to mature into antigen-specific cells – cells that can recognise and respond to a specific antigen – which are ready to take up their vital role in the immune system. The mature T lymphocytes eventually enter the medulla, and migrate through the walls of tiny blood and lymph vessels to elsewhere in the circulation where they will await the call for action.*

33

The spleen

In addition to the millions of blood cells that die or are damaged every day, the blood picks up pathogens from the skin, intestines, lungs and many other places. The job of filtering out all this waste material falls to the spleen.

BAG OF BLOOD

The spleen is the largest lymphoid organ in the body. It is supplied with a great many blood vessels and its high blood content gives it a deep red colour. Unfortunately, the spleen is quite a vulnerable organ and is easily ruptured. Lying along the side of the stomach, between the stomach, the ribs and the diaphragm, the spleen is not well protected against injury. In addition, it is encased in only a thin capsule – a fibrous outer wrapping – and if this is pierced it is hard for a surgeon to repair it because the spleen bleeds so heavily. A ruptured spleen may have to be removed entirely. Luckily, the functions of the spleen can be carried on by other lymphoid tissues, although a person without a spleen is far more liable to catch an infection.

PULP FACTS

The spleen performs a similar function for the blood to that which the lymph nodes perform for the lymph. It filters out germs, dirt and dead or damaged blood cells, and functions as a base for launching specific immune responses to infections affecting the blood. Blood flows in via the splenic artery and passes through areas of lymphoid tissue called white pulp, where lymphocytes keep watch for blood-borne antigens. Then the blood flows through areas of red pulp, where white blood cells of all sorts clean and filter the blood. The spleen also stores millions of red blood cells and platelets, as a reservoir for when stocks run low.

Spleen

Stomach

MALTS AND GALT

Along the digestive, respiratory and urogenital tracts, lymph cells aggregate into patches of lymphoid tissue that are larger than lymph nodes. These lymphoid tissues are strategically located wherever tracts communicate with the external environment, providing a possible route for pathogens to get into the body. Mucosa-associated lymphoid tissues (MALTs) include the five tonsils on the wall of the pharynx, and the spleen. They also include gut-associated lymphatic tissue (GALT), found along the intestines, which secretes antibodies into the gut to help to fight off gut bacteria that try to enter the bloodstream by crossing the intestinal walls.

The spleen can store up to 5 million red blood cells.

White pulp *is lymphoid tissue. As blood passes through areas of white pulp in the spleen, lymphocytes in the white pulp keep watch for blood-borne antigens which may trigger the immune system to deal with an infection. About a quarter of the body's entire store of lymphoid tissue is in the spleen.*

Red pulp *makes up three-quarters of the spleen. It derives its colour from the high concentration of red blood cells contained within it, but it is white cells in the red pulp that have the task of cleaning and filtering the blood.*

The splenic artery *is the principal highway down which blood travels into the spleen.*

The splenic vein *drains blood away from the spleen and into the venous system that carries it towards the heart.*

The largest lymphoid organ in the body
About 12cm (5in) long, the spleen normally weighs around 150g (5oz), although in its capacity as a blood reserve it can hold as much as a litre, and therefore weigh over a kilogram.

Antibodies

If white blood cells are like soldiers, antibodies are the weapons they use – weapons of simple design but incredible sophistication, individually tailored to hunt, target and destroy anything that threatens your health.

FORM AND FUNCTION

Antibodies, technically called immunoglobulins (shortened to Ig), are large proteins produced by mature B lymphocytes (often simply called B cells). They help the immune system to recognise and target antigens, and also help in the attack directly. Humans have five different types of antibodies, known as IgA, IgD, IgE, IgG and IgM. Each is found in different parts of the body and they have slightly different, though often overlapping, functions. However, the basic structure of each antibody is very similar.

SPECIFIC BY DESIGN

Your body makes antibodies against millions of different antigens, including many that it has never before encountered, and yet each one is specific for its target antigen. Where does this diversity come from? Although each antibody has the same basic structure, key regions of each have variable structures. The genes that code for these variable regions can be shuffled and rearranged differently in each antibody-producing B cell to give millions of possible combinations – enough to account for almost any possible antigen that you will encounter during your lifetime.

LINES OF ATTACK

As soon as an antibody encounters and binds to its antigen it can start to attack it in several different ways:

- **Agglutination** Antibodies have two binding sites (some classes have more), and so can bind to two antigens at once. With enough antibodies, groups of antigens can be stuck together in clumps, preventing them from attacking the body and making them easy targets for other weapons in the immune system.
- **Enhancing recognition** Cells of the immune system have difficulty recognising antigens until they have formed antigen/antibody complexes, which trigger them into action.
- **Neutralisation** By covering the active parts of a molecule of toxin, antibodies can render it harmless.
- **Activation of complement** The complement system is a chain of reactions between blood-borne proteins called complement factors, which leads to the production of potent corrosive enzymes that lock on to and destroy antigens.

Your body has the capacity to produce more than 100 million different antibodies.

A plasma cell – a mature B lymphocyte – *producing antibodies. Each plasma cell can produce 2000 antibody molecules per second.*

MEMORIES

The immune system can remember antigens that it has faced in the past, making it more prepared to meet the next attack. The population of B cells in the blood is always changing, with new strains replacing old ones. B cells that have been activated, however, are preserved and kept on standby, and are even refined so they produce antibodies that bind more easily and tightly to antigens. As a result, if you encounter the same antigen again, your immune system is able to mount a quicker and more powerful response than it did the first time.

The antigen binding site
at the tip of each of the two prong-like light chains has a specially shaped cavity moulded to fit with a specific antigen. If the antibody comes into contact with its target antigen, it locks onto it, forming an antigen/antibody complex, and triggers one of a number of possible immune response strategies.

Antigen

Antibody

The 'variable portion' *of the antibody – the upper region of the light chain – is the part that differs between each antibody, making it specific for one antigen. The rest of the antibody forms the 'constant portion' – an area that is the same in all IgG antibodies.*

Proteins known as 'light chains' *are attached to the top of the heavy chains, to make up the arms of the antibody.*

The 'hinge region' *allows the arms of the antibody to move about, making it easier for them to latch onto two antigens at once.*

A typical antibody
The antibody shown here is of the IgG type – the most common type in the body, making up 75 per cent of the antibodies in your bloodstream. It displays the classic Y-shape of the antibody molecule.

A pair of proteins known as 'heavy chains' *makes up the main stalk of the antibody. The stalk is involved in the activation of complement and attachment to cell membranes.*

A day in the life of the blood and immune system

The components of your blood and immune system interact in a complex web, as white and red blood cells and plasma proteins move back and forth between the bloodstream and the tissues, warding off potential threats from the environment that bombard your system.

ETERNAL VIGILANCE

A system as complex as your body is inevitably vulnerable to upset, and disruption to any one factor can have knock-on effects on others. It is vital, therefore, that your immune system is vigilant at all times, and its responses are coordinated for maximum efficiency. With such powerful biological agents, however, there's always a risk that they could accidentally attack or damage parts of your own system in an autoimmune reaction. Your immune system has built-in safeguards to prevent this, but allergic reactions are examples of what happens when these safeguards aren't working properly.

08:00 Cuts like a knife

While fixing a packed lunch, your hand slips and you cut yourself. The wound bleeds freely until you apply a dressing. Your body's leak prevention system springs into action as soon as the knife goes in. Platelets and clotting factors are immediately activated, and within a minute or so a clot of fibrin molecules and platelets blocks the tear in the blood vessel wall. White blood cells, attracted by chemical signals given off by the clotting agents, move in around the clot and clear away any germs or dirt.

13:00 Restocking

Your spinach and ricotta salad is packed with iron, which is good because your body has been tapping its stores to help replace the lost blood cells (and their precious cargo of haemoglobin). Soon after you cut yourself, sensory cells in your kidneys detected that the oxygen carrying capacity of your blood was down, and stimulated your bone marrow to churn out red blood cells at a faster rate. Meanwhile your liver increases its production of plasma proteins. The lost blood is quickly replaced.

16:00 Summer in the city

By mid-afternoon the pollen count is high and your hay fever starts to kick in. Antibodies of the IgE class (in the lining of your nasal passages) bind to antigens on the surfaces of the pollen grains. This activates mast cells, which release their granules of histamine. The flood of histamine irritates the nasal lining and triggers mucus production and then a sneeze, as well as activating your tear glands. Luckily your hay fever is mild, and other immune system cells release soothing signalling chemicals that suppress the activity of the mast cells and the B cells that make IgE.

Shower power

Studies have shown that taking regular cold showers or baths can reduce your chances of catching a cold. If this sounds too painful, try turning your shower to cold for a few seconds just before you get out – this will stimulate the movement of blood around your system.

20:00 Down and dirty

A tackle during your weekly soccer game sends you sprawling in the mud, and dirt gets into the cut on your hand. Soil bacteria now find themselves in a richly nutritious environment, but your immune defences quickly swing into action. Your wound is already full of neutrophils and monocytes – between them they make short work of the invading microbes. Neutrophils bathe them in corrosive enzymes, while the monocytes consume them and display their antigens to other immune system cells. The monocytes also release chemotaxins: signalling substances that attract other cells to the area, particularly fibroblasts, which make scar tissue, walling off the wound and preventing more bacteria from getting in.

18:00 Holiday jab

After work you keep your appointment at the local health clinic, where you receive the first of the vaccinations needed for your upcoming holiday. In the days following the injection, the antigenic material that is in the vaccine will stimulate the production of antibodies (protein molecules synthesised in lymphoid tissue) that, should you become exposed to antigens belonging to the disease while you are abroad, will fight off the illness.

2

Healthy systems for life

TAKE CHARGE OF YOUR HEALTH

The good news as far as the immune system is concerned is that there is a lot you can do on a daily basis to keep it working efficiently, so that it can do its job of protecting you from niggling infections, from more serious health problems, and from the potentially harmful effects of the environmental hazards around you.

 43 *Prevention is always better than cure, so spotting signs of potential problems early pays huge dividends.*

 47 *Healthy blood can only do its job if the system that pumps it is healthy too. Keeping blood pressure controlled is a key step.*

 49 *Knowing the risks from the environment and how carcinogens invade the body can help you steer clear of potential health hazards.*

 51 *Understanding the highly specialised nature of the cells of the immune system can help you to support it every day of your life.*

 55 *When individuals donate blood, they can be sure that it will be taken safely, analysed professionally and used to help others.*

Knowing what's normal for you

The signs and symptoms of a blood disorder, or of the immune system not fighting off infection as it should, are often quite subtle. Knowing what is to be expected may help you to spot when something is amiss.

The health of your blood and immune system has an enormous impact on your general well-being. Your energy levels and your ability to fight off minor and more serious illnesses both depend on the health of your immune system.

NORMAL BLEEDING

The bleeding from a minor cut, such as inflicted while shaving or pricking yourself on a thorn in the garden, should stop fairly fast. Even a deeper cut – as long as pressure is applied with a clean cloth – should stop bleeding within about seven minutes or so. A deep cut may well bleed longer; if it soaks through your first cloth, add a second on top (leave the first one in place). Blood from a minor cut that takes a long time to clot could signal a problem and you should see your GP about this.

People who have problems with their blood clotting properly usually notice bleeding from minor injuries in different parts of the body, together with excessive bruising. Women with periods that are heavier than usual may have a gynaecological problem, but again, a problem with clotting may cause excessively heavy periods.

You should consult your doctor about any unexplained bleeding, whether it clots quickly or not.

Bleeding from the ears or nose

Bleeding from an ear is never normal and should be investigated urgently by a doctor. Nosebleeds, on the other hand, are usually harmless. However, a nosebleed may require a doctor's attention if:
- blood flows from both nostrils;
- blood is also running down the back of the throat;
- bleeding is still going on 30 minutes after it started;
- the nosebleed keeps recurring over the next few days.

Bleeding from the gums

Bleeding from the gums is not normal beyond a small amount caused by over-enthusiastic brushing of the teeth. More than this is most likely due to gum disease – generally gingivitis – especially if the gums are swollen, tender or painful. Anyone who suspects they have gum disease should see their dentist as soon as possible to get any infection cleared up; otherwise their teeth may loosen and fall out or have to be removed by the dentist. Bleeding gums that are painless may be a symptom of a problem with blood failing to clot as it should normally.

HOW EASILY DO YOU BRUISE?

Bruising is caused by bleeding into the tissues under the skin. Some bruising is perfectly normal: for example, after a knock or a fall. People tend to bruise more easily

Gently does it
There's a fine line between effective teeth cleaning and over-brushing which causes gums to bleed. If teeth regularly bleed after brushing, try a softer brush to see if that helps, otherwise consult a dentist.

HOW TIRED IS TOO TIRED?

Many factors contribute to excessive fatigue: the feeling that you simply can't get out of bed in the morning. In many cases, however, simple lifestyle practices can make an enormous difference to energy levels.

BEAT STRESS AND ANXIETY
Stress is a major cause of fatigue, while worrying about personal problems can exacerbate tiredness. Get help to deal with stress and anxiety, devise a stress management programme, or take up meditation, yoga or tai chi.

GET ENOUGH SLEEP
Most adults need a minimum of seven hours a night of quality sleep. If you are short-changing yourself on this, fatigue can build. Keep the bedroom cool and well ventilated and try to establish a regular time to go to bed and to get up.

as they get older because the tissues under the skin grow looser. Those who regularly take steroid drugs may also bruise more easily than normal. A younger person not taking steroid drugs who bruises easily may have a problem with blood clotting that warrants further investigation. Unexplained bruising should be brought to the attention of a doctor, as should any bruise that does not begin to improve within a fortnight or has not cleared completely within a month.

SWOLLEN LYMPH GLANDS
The commonest cause of swollen lymph glands is infection. For example, a sore throat caused by a viral infection will cause swelling of the lymph glands in the neck. The glands may be tender to touch. This shouldn't alarm you or cause you to go your GP. But swollen lymph glands can also be caused by a more serious infection and, sometimes, cancer. In this case, the lymph glands all over the body may be swollen, they may be tender and the swelling will not disappear after a few days, as in normal infections. If you have these symptoms, consult your GP.

COLD EXTREMITIES
When you go out into the cold, it is normal for your body to reduce the amount of blood reaching your hands and feet. This is the body's automatic response to cold, designed to protect the vital internal organs, such as the brain, liver and kidneys. Sometimes you may notice that your hands change colour and become numb or even painful. All this can be normal; it tends to be more common in women than in men.

It is not normal for hands to stay painful for several minutes after they have been warmed up – this may signal Raynaud's phenomenon (see page 151). If your fingers or toes are beginning to show signs of damage from the cold – by developing chilblains, for example – you should seek medical advice.

Prevention is always better than cure with cold extremities: dress appropriately and try exercises to improve the circulation (see pages 77 and 79).

GET SOME EXERCISE
Paradoxically, exercise makes you less — rather than more — tired. Try to build regular exercise, ideally in the fresh air, into your daily life. It does not have to be a sporting activity — 30 minutes gardening still counts as exercise.

DRINK SMART
Caffeine is often used for a quick lift — but it stays in the bloodstream for up to eight hours. If you are not sleeping well, avoid tea or coffee after lunchtime. Alcohol, too, can interrupt sleep patterns. Instead drink plenty of water throughout the day.

EAT WELL
Have a sizeable, fibre-rich breakfast to give you the energy to start the day, then eat regular high-carbohydrate meals and snacks. Avoid high-fat, high-sugar foods which may make you feel energised in the short term, but will lead to sluggishness when their 'buzz' wears off.

INFECTIONS IN CHILDREN
It is normal for children to pick up frequent infections, from babyhood onwards. This is because they have not yet been exposed to most micro-organisms and are only gradually building up their immunity. However, if your child is spending more time with a runny nose or sore throat than without, it may be a good idea to consult your GP, just in case the child's immune system is not functioning as it should be. This is especially so if a child is not growing or putting on weight as expected, or if a child's mental development appears to be slightly delayed.

A child who is suffering from a particularly severe infection should see a doctor, especially if there is fever or a rash as well, or the child is markedly more quiet and subdued than normal.

INFECTIONS IN ADULTS
The process of catching infections and building up immunity continues throughout adult life. Sometimes a virus will lie dormant in our bodies and become active later; this is normal. One example of this is the chickenpox virus, which can become active as shingles (more than two attacks of shingles a year may mean a problem with the immune system).

GETTING TIRED
It can be very difficult to work out whether tiredness is normal or not. Most of us feel tired some of the time, especially when we're bringing up children as well as working hard outside the home. However, if you feel tired after several nights of eight hours of uninterrupted sleep, there may be a problem.

If you have to nap for a few minutes during the day, or doing routine tasks makes you exhausted, you may be suffering from excessive fatigue. Keeping a diary of how tired you are and what makes you feel extra tired can help to clarify the issue in your mind. It may also help to convince your doctor that something is amiss. Excessive fatigue can be caused by problems such as anaemia, an underactive thyroid gland, infection or chronic fatigue syndrome (see page 140).

LIFESTYLE FACTORS AND ANAEMIA

Someone becomes anaemic when there is a shortage of oxygen-carrying haemoglobin in the blood, which means that tissues throughout the body become deprived of the oxygen they need in order to function effectively. The chief symptom is usually fatigue, regardless of how much sleep you are getting.

Anaemia is a symptom, rather than a condition, so diagnosing someone as anaemic will prompt further investigations into their state of health.

The only way to confirm a case of anaemia is to have a full blood count (see page 105). This will check whether your haemoglobin is at the right level for your sex and age. It is sensible to have this test if you have symptoms that suggest anaemia (see page 134), particularly excessive fatigue, or if you have a condition which may cause anaemia.

A full blood count can also provide information on the cause of anaemia. For example, if the red blood cells in the sample are unusually small, this shows a deficiency in iron. A patient will then be asked whether he or she has experienced excessive bleeding, and their diet will be assessed. The treatment for anaemia caused by iron deficiency is a simple and effective course of iron tablets.

Can pregnancy make a woman anaemic?

Pregnancy increases the risk of anaemia because there is an increase in demand for iron and other vitamins. The iron needed to make haemoglobin in the blood is distributed to both the mother and her baby. This results in the woman's own iron levels being reduced, leading to anaemia. Iron can be easily replaced by supplements or changes to the diet. Folic acid is another key component of haemoglobin, and a deficiency can also lead to anaemia.

Can losing blood cause anaemia?

Excessive bleeding (heavy periods, or blood loss during surgery) can cause anaemia by depleting the body's stores of iron. Small cuts, such as those you can get while cooking, will not cause anaemia.

What are the signs or symptoms to look out for?

The main symptoms of iron deficiency anaemia are very pale skin, an increase in the number of minor infections, weakness, fatigue, tiredness and breathlessness on slight effort.

Can lifestyle affect iron levels?

An imbalanced diet can lead to iron deficiency.

Is it possible to eat a good, balanced diet, yet still suffer from low iron levels and anaemia?

Nutrients can be poorly absorbed because of a disorder or disease of the gut, leading to deficiencies that can cause anaemia. For example, pernicious anaemia (see page 151) is caused by cells that help absorb vitamin B_{12} having been damaged by the immune system, leading to vitamin B_{12} deficiency.

Can anaemia be a symptom of more serious conditions?

Blood diseases such as leukaemia also cause anaemia.

Keeping blood pressure under control

High blood pressure, or hypertension, is a common condition that over time can damage the arteries, brain, kidneys and heart. The consequences of uncontrolled hypertension include coronary artery disease and strokes.

The majority of cases of high blood pressure (hypertension) are not caused by any particular disease. Instead, people with high blood pressure tend to fall into at least one of the following categories:

- they have a family history of high blood pressure;
- they tend to eat a lot of salt;
- they are overweight;
- they do not take much exercise;
- they experience high stress levels;
- they drink alcohol to excess;
- they smoke.

Relatively rarely, hypertension may be caused by diseases that affect organs such as the kidneys and adrenal glands (which secrete blood pressure controlling hormones).

BLOOD PRESSURE CHECKS

- Healthy people under the age of 45 should have their blood pressure checked every two years. Because hypertension may cause no noticeable symptoms, having a regular check is an easy way to pick up any unhealthy rise in blood pressure before the complications of hypertension develop.
- People at risk of hypertension because of family history or lifestyle should have their blood pressure measured more frequently – at least once a year, sometimes more – as should those who have a family history of heart disease or problems with the blood vessels, kidneys or endocrine system.

- Pregnant women should have their blood pressure checked at each clinic visit, because high blood pressure can be dangerous for both mother and baby.

Although you can buy blood pressure measuring devices, it's best to have blood pressure measured by a medical professional, who is trained in the technique and will use equipment that is checked for accuracy.

For some people the stress of just visiting the doctor can push up their blood pressure (so-called white-coat hypertension). If your blood pressure is high on a single occasion, a second test will be arranged; try to make sure you are able to rest and relax for a few minutes before the test. If you have hypertension, your doctor may set up urine and blood tests to rule out underlying diseases. There may also be tests to check for complications following on from the hypertension, such as a heart trace.

NORMAL BLOOD PRESSURE

There are two parts to the measurement of blood pressure. The first is the systolic reading, taken as the heart beats, and the second is the diastolic reading, taken as the heart muscle relaxes again.

Blood pressure does vary enormously from individual to individual and over time. There are some general guidelines, however.

- A healthy blood pressure is a systolic reading of less than 130, and a diastolic reading of less than 85 (this will be expressed as 130/85).

- Your doctor may recommend lifestyle changes if your blood pressure reaches 140/90.
- Medication will probably be prescribed when blood pressure reaches 160/100. An individual with blood pressure at this level is not considered a good candidate for surgery, so medication to lower it and keep it down will be needed if any surgery is being planned.

Try to keep calm during a test
Blood pressure measurements vary throughout the day, depending on activity level and even your emotional state. Blood pressure is lower during periods of sleep and usually rises in response to exercise.

Weight control
Maintain your weight within the healthy weight range for your height and sex.

Stress buster
Find some practical ways for managing stress that work for you and put them into practice.

Salt alert
Reduce your salt intake – this may require advice from a dietitian, but a simple effective strategy is to cut down on processed foods and snacks. Experts suggest limiting daily intake to about 5g – a slightly heaped teaspoon.

WHAT YOU CAN DO TO KEEP BLOOD PRESSURE WITHIN HEALTHY LIMITS

There is good evidence that anti-hypertensive drugs control blood pressure and reduce the risk of the side effects of hypertension. But, apart from drugs, there is a lot that you can do to treat your own hypertension, or to reduce the chances of developing hypertension in the first place.

Know the risks
Hypertension runs in families, so if your parents suffered, you might too. Have your blood pressure checked regularly, particularly over the age of 45.

Limit alcohol intake
Keep your alcohol intake within guidelines – if you want to control your blood pressure you probably shouldn't drink more than a glass of wine a day, with some alcohol-free days each week.

Get moving
Do brisk exercise for 30 minutes, three times a week. This does not mean going to the gym if you don't want to: walking and gardening are both good forms of exercise.

Eat smart
Reducing fat and increasing fibre won't directly help your blood pressure, but it will reduce the risk of heart attacks.

Quit smoking
Smoking is a major contributor to high blood pressure. Use every available resource to stop smoking cigarettes.

Be aware of risk factors

The world around us contains many threats to the health of our blood and lymph systems. General pollutants can contaminate air, water or soil, while smoking and drinking too much alcohol can impact on others as well as ourselves.

Chemicals, bacteria, viruses, drugs and toxins can all trigger problems in the immune system.

CARCINOGENS

Carcinogens are substances that increase the risk of cancer developing, usually by causing damage to the DNA within cell nuclei. Some scientists suggest that carcinogens leave the way open for cancer cells to appear and multiply by damaging the immune system. However this is a possibile – not the usual – cause of cancer. Patients with severely damaged immune systems – due to HIV or immune suppressive drugs, for example – are at higher risk of developing cancer than other people. Conversely, only a few cancers, such as lymphoma (see page 150), myeloma (see page 150) and chronic lymphatic leukemia (see page 148) cause significant damage to the immune system.

Cigarette smoking

Cigarette smoke is a potent carcinogen. One in ten smokers will develop cancer of the lungs, tongue, stomach or bladder. Smoking also causes cancer of the kidney, pancreas, liver and nose, and leukaemia.

Alcohol

Alcohol is a carcinogen linked to cancer of the oesophagus and breast. In addition, alcohol depresses zinc levels, which is essential to the healthy functioning of the immune system. However, moderate drinking – say one drink a day, particularly a glass of red wine with a meal – can actually improve your state of health.

Medicines

All medicinal drugs are thoroughly tested for carcinogenicity before they become available to patients. Some types of chemotherapy, used to treat cancer, do increase the risk of another cancer developing several years later. However, potential risks are always carefully assessed before treatment starts. More usually, bone marrow failure (see page 138) is a consequence of taking these drugs.

EXTERNAL THREATS

The world around us can also have an enormous impact on health. However there are many things we can do to reduce potential risks.

Lead poisoning

Taking in too much lead poses a particular threat to children, who are more likely to suffer ill-effects than adults. Lead poisoning can cause a type of anaemia and brain damage.

FOR BABIES

Protecting babies from lead in tap water

Bottle-fed babies are at risk of lead poisoning if the tap water that is added to their formula has any lead in it. So, too, are babies who drink water or juice mixed with water, even if they are mainly breastfed. Boiling drinking water may kill bacteria, but it does not get rid of the lead content.
To protect your baby:
• If there is reason to suspect that the water in your home is passing through lead piping (as in many older buildings) or a leaded solder has been used to seal water pipe joints (as is done illegally in some new houses), get the lead levels tested by the local authority or water company. If levels are high, the cause should be established and any affected piping or solder replaced.

• Wherever you are, only take drinking water from the cold water tap in the kitchen. Let the water run for a good minute before taking any water. If in doubt, prepare feeds from bottled water.

MINIMISING YOUR RISKS

There is a lot you can do to limit your exposure to potential threats, and in some cases remove them altogether from your environment.

Have any lead pipes in your house replaced; if you are unsure, the Drinking Water Inspectorate can detail what to look for.

In a house built before 1970, make sure all flaking paint is well sealed.

The risk to health of radiation from radon, naturally emitted from granite rocks, is tiny...

...However if your home is on granite, it can be tested for radon and advice will be given on sealing the ground floor and ventilation.

There is little evidence that mobile phones are harmful to health, but little that they are safe either. The government recommends limiting their use by children.

Lead poisoning is less of a threat than it once was since it has been withdrawn from petrol and paints no longer contain lead. Lead-contaminated drinking water may be a problem in buildings with lead in the plumbing system.

Radiation

There are many forms of radiation including ionising radiation (X-rays and rays from nuclear reactions), electromagnetic radiation (from electrical currents) and microwaves (from mobile phones, for example). Like chemical carcinogens, radiation can cause cancer by damaging the DNA within cells.

There is no doubt that large, concentrated doses of radiation are harmful. However, there is as yet little evidence of an increased incidence of blood disorders, cancer or problems with the immune system in those who have been exposed to ionising radiation accidentally released into the atmosphere.

Much of the controversy around radiation in the UK has centred on the Sellafield nuclear processing plant in Cumbria. A study in 1999 examined the health of 470 workers, and found no increased rate of any form of cancer, compared to the national average. There has also been concern that people living in the area may have been exposed to long-term higher levels of radiation. Research has failed to show that these people have had any increased risk of developing cancer.

Other studies, however, have revealed that levels of leukaemia and lymphoma (cancer in the lymph nodes) in children living in the area are higher than the national average. It has been suggested this may be due to fathers of affected children having been damaged by radiation, but research has not revealed any direct evidence to support this. Another theory suggests that the many 'outsiders' who moved into the area to take up work at the plant in the 1950s naturally brought all sorts of viruses with them, and this increased leukaemia and lymphoma levels.

Gulf War syndrome

TALKING POINT

During the Gulf War of 1991, troops were exposed to many chemicals and pollutants. Pesticides were used extensively. The many oil well fires exposed soldiers to pollutants caused by petroleum combustion. Drinking water was contaminated or over-chlorinated; vehicles were sprayed with camouflage paint. Soldiers were also given vaccines designed to protect them from disease and from chemical attack.

After the war, thousands of veterans suffered a variety of symptoms — including fatigue, joint pain, skin problems, depression and memory loss — termed Gulf War syndrome. Lawyers acting for some soldiers have suggested that the chemicals to which they were exposed may have damaged their nervous systems, or the multiple vaccines may have over-stimulated or exhausted their immune systems, leading to their health problems. So far, however, scientists have not proven a definite link between Gulf War syndrome and either vaccines or chemicals.

A healthy immune system

The immune system fights off infection, which involves eliminating anything foreign to the body. It also remembers what it has met before; this allows a vigorous response when a foreign body is encountered for the second time.

The body's war against infection is fought by cells and proteins carried in body fluids. Key players include:
- phagocytes
- complement proteins
- T cells
- antibodies.

The role of phagocytes
Phagocytes are cells in our body fluids that track down and engulf microorganisms such as bacteria and fungi. The name phagocyte comes from the Greek words meaning 'eating cells'. Without phagocytes our bodies would be overwhelmed by infection. If not treated, a patient who develops neutropenia – a deficiency of phagocytes – would probably die of infection within just a few hours.

The role of complement proteins
Invading microorganisms that are too fast for the phagocytes are attacked by a group of proteins called complement proteins. These can be found at any place in the body where a foreign cell can gain access and cause infection, such as the mucous membranes lining the mouth or gut. Just a few bacteria can activate millions of complement proteins, and the complement proteins attract phagocytes to the site of infection to finish the job of destroying invading microorganisms.

T cells versus viruses
Viruses can only live and reproduce inside cells, and are totally dependent on the host cell's machinery for all their needs. Living only inside cells means they cannot be identified as invaders by that body's phagocytes and complement proteins. It is likely that the T cell evolved to overcome this problem; it is T cells that detect and kill cells infected with viruses.

Antibodies and allergic reactions
Antibodies are special kinds of proteins that help the immune system to recognise, target and attack any substance that the body regards as foreign or possibly dangerous (see page 36). They are produced by a type of white blood cell called a B cell. Any substance that provokes an attack from an antibody is known as an antigen.

Normally antibodies react to and destroy antigens in your body without you experiencing any side effects. Sometimes, however, certain antigens cause the body to overreact.

Keep it moderate
Regular exercise improves blood circulation and boosts the speed with which the immune system responds to invaders. Some studies have shown light to moderate exercise to be more beneficial than more intense workouts.

FOR BABIES

Breastfeeding and the immune system

Unborn babies are connected to their mother by the placenta. The IgG class of antibody travels from the mother, across the placenta and into the unborn baby, so that at birth a baby has some immunity to infection (a child's own immune system is not mature until about the age of five). After birth, a mother passes antibodies of the IgA class to her baby in her breast milk. Breast milk contains antibodies to fight every infection to which the mother has been exposed. Together, the IgG and IgA antibodies give breastfed babies greater levels of immunity. This method of passing on immunity is shared by all mammals, who feed their babies on milk.

Whenever these particular antigens (called allergens) are encountered, a type of antibody called IgE provokes a dramatic response as the body seeks to expel the allergen. The classic example is hayfever, in which IgE antibodies trigger the expulsion of the pollen allergen through a runny nose and sneezing. This type of overreaction is referred to as hypersensitivity.

Fighting the common cold

The reason that a cold usually lasts only three or four days is because T cells clear the virus that caused it. In the process of killing the virus, T cells divide many times over and by the end of the process there will be several million T cells capable of recognising that specific cold virus. Some of these T cells survive for many years. This means that if you are exposed to the same virus again, your immune system will respond more quickly, and you will not suffer a full-blown cold from that virus again. Unfortunately, there are many different strains of cold virus, which is why we keep on catching colds.

WHEN THE IMMUNE SYSTEM TURNS ON ITSELF

The vast majority of immune responses are helpful, enabling our bodies to eliminate infections and cancerous cells. Almost all T cells and antibodies are conditioned not to attack any cells produced by the host's own body. For T cells this conditioning takes place within the thymus (an organ just behind the breast bone); for antibodies it happens in the bone marrow.

Inevitably, however, the body does produce some T cells and antibodies that will target harmless cells belonging to the host's own body. The immune system gets round this by ordering these autoimmune T and B cells to self-destruct.

However, antibodies and T cells do sometimes attack the body's own tissues, giving rise to a variety of disorders loosely termed 'autoimmune diseases'. Perhaps the best-known examples of autoimmune diseases are pernicious anaemia, rheumatic fever, rheumatoid arthritis and SLE (systemic lupus erythematosus).

IMMUNOLOGICAL MEMORY

The body's ability to defend itself against invaders such as bacteria and viruses is called immunity. The human immune system can remember most invaders it has encountered before: a second encounter with the same agent prompts a rapid immune response. This is called immunological memory, and means that an individual effectively becomes immune to a particular toxin.

Immunisation and vaccines

By taking advantage of immunological memory, vaccines do not need to contain live, potentially dangerous microorganisms. Instead, they utilise proteins from microorganisms to stimulate immunological memory. Vaccines are the major immunological success story of the last century and have saved many hundreds of millions of lives (see pages 88–91).

UNDERSTANDING THREATS TO YOUR IMMUNE SYSTEM

The immune system is integral to the efficient functioning of every part of your body – even your brain. If you are suffering from an infection, for example, the immune system instructs the brain to raise your body temperature in an attempt to destroy the invading organism; this is why fever is such a classic symptom of infection. In addition, when you have a fever the immune system directs the brain to make you feel tired so that you will sleep more, and reduces your appetite so that you eat less.

Conversely, many behaviours, disorders and medical treatments that affect your various body systems will also affect the immune system.

- Any kind of stress will have negative effects on the immune system. Experiments have shown that even a short stressful stimulus, such as a loud noise, sends signals to the brain and endocrine glands and has a measurable negative effect on the immune system. More prolonged stress has more serious effects. For example, the psychological stress of bereavement can weaken the immune system.

- Excessive exercise may depress the immune system. Athletes suffer more coughs and colds while training for competitions than at other times. This is one reason why exercise has to be balanced and why it is not good to push yourself too hard (see pages 84–85).

- Repeated use of some drugs to treat infections – notably steroids and broad-spectrum antibiotics – can destroy beneficial bacteria in the gut; these bacteria play an important role in the functioning of the immune system. Probiotics can help to redress the balance.

- Areas of localised infection – such as dental abcesses or infected tonsils – may disturb the normal immune system processes of neutralising and eliminating an infection.

- When you cough, you are clearing the airways and lungs of infected matter. Cough suppression medications block this natural process, so that infection is not expelled as it should be, and the efficiency of the immune system is consequently lowered.

- People who take large qantities of herbs need to know about possible side effects – for example, large quantities of liquorice can lead to salt retention and high blood pressure. Many experts believe that relaxation techniques are a safer and more effective complementary therapy for the immune system.

Herbs that may boost the immune system

Many people take herbs for an immune system boost, and often feel better for it, but no herb should be taken to excess.

Astralagus root (*Astralagus membranaceus*)
Some people believe that Chinese astralagus root – also known as milk vetch – ia a powerful stimulator of the immune system in general. It is often used to ward off or treat the common cold.

Echinacea (*Echinacea angustifolia*)
This wildflower from North America, the purple coneflower, is thought to be one of the most effective and popular enhancers of the immune system used in the West. It is believed to trigger resistance against colds, flu and many other infections.

Usnea (*Usnea barbata*)
A common lichen, usnea is an immune system tonic that particularly targets bacterial infections, but it may be of overall benefit whenever the body is fighting infection.

Poke root (*Phytolacca americana*)
Herbalists believe that poke root tincture is best used to counter infections centred on the throat, chest and lungs. It works well when taken with echinacea.

Ginseng root (*Panax ginseng*)
As well as stimulating non-specific resistance to infection, this Chinese herb has traditionally been used to help the body fight fatigue and stress (though there is little scientific evidence of its effectiveness as an energy-booster).

Garlic (*Allium sativum*)
Garlic is an antiseptic and blood cleanser, good for catarrhal infections. Tablets made from freeze-dried garlic do not cause the breath problems associated with fresh garlic.

Liquorice (*Glycyrrhiza glabra*)
This herb helps the immune system by stimulating the formation of white blood cells and antibodies. In particular, it fights infection within the respiratory tract. It also stimulates production of energy-boosting adrenaline.

LIFESTYLE SUPPORT FOR THE IMMUNE SYSTEM

As well as avoiding behaviours that increase your susceptibility to infection, you can also take various positive measures to strengthen the response of your immune system to infection.

EAT A BALANCED DIET

A balanced diet is just one important contribution you can make to ensure you have a healthy immune system. To make sure you have a good balance of vitamins and minerals, including micronutrients such as zinc, eat a mixed diet that's low in fat, with adequate amounts of protein and carbohydrate, and plenty of fruit and vegetables. This should maintain the immune system in good order without recourse to dietary additives or supplements. In fact, some nutrients – such as vitamin D – can damage your immune system and other body systems if taken in excess.

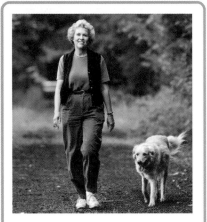

RELAX – DON'T DO IT

As stress is known to hinder the immune system, learning to relax should improve its functioning – even though there is no hard evidence of this from clinical trials. Take time to find a way of relaxing that works for you. This could be anything from yoga to a gentle walk in the park with the dog.

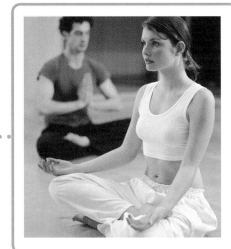

VISUALISATION TECHNIQUES

The power of the mind can bolster the immune system by means of 'creative visualisation' or 'guided imagery'. Concentrating on relaxing images is a good way to reduce stress levels, which benefits the immune system. Scientific evidence is lacking, however, on whether focusing your thoughts on boosting your body's defences – visualising a virus being chased out of your bloodstream, for example – can really improve your body's ability to resist infection or not.

HYDROTHERAPY

Research has shown that regular cold baths or showers and swimming in cold water have a stimulating effect on the immune system. One study that compared university students who had a daily cold bath with those who did not showed that the cold bath takers suffered from significantly fewer colds.

LIGHT

There is some evidence that people who live and work in artificial light have more infections that those who experience lots of daylight, pointing to the importance of sunlight to the immune system.

Why give blood?

Hospitals in England alone need about 10,000 donations every day for life-saving operations and procedures, yet figures from the Blood Transfusion Service show that only 6 per cent of the population give blood regularly.

Milestones
IN MEDICINE

In 1901 Karl Landsteiner discovered the first human blood group system, which he called the ABO system. He defined four basic groups within this system: A, B, AB, and O. 'Landsteiner's law' was based on the discovery that blood clumping, or agglutination, occurs during a transfusion when the recipient carries antibodies against the donor blood cells. Specifically, the plasma of a person contains natural antibodies to A or B if those antigens are absent from that person's red cells.

WHAT HAPPENS WHEN YOU GIVE BLOOD?

In the United Kingdom, blood donation is entirely voluntary. The Blood Transfusion Service operates a donor selection policy that protects the health of both the blood donor and the recipient. There are strict donor selection guidelines. Donors are asked to fill out a donor session slip and answer pertinent questions, in private, relating to their health. A first-time or returning donor (lapsed for more than two years), will have to answer more questions than a regular donor. When there is concern for the health of a donor or potential recipient, the donor may be permanently excluded or deferred for a defined period. A short term deferral can occur if you are anaemic or have a cold or the flu on the day.

The ideal donor will be between 17 and 70 years old (but first time donors are not taken over the age of 60) and should weigh over 50kg (7st 12lb). Each donor's blood is tested for HIV, hepatitis B, hepatitis C and syphilis. If any test gives a positive result, further testing will be necessary. Donors are permanently excluded if:
- they are HIV positive;
- they are hepatitis B or C carriers;
- they are males who have ever had oral or anal sex with another man;
- they have ever received money or drugs for sex;
- they have ever injected drugs (including body-building drugs).

Donors are deferred for 12 months if:
- they are women who have had sex with a man who has ever had oral or anal sex with another man;
- they have had sex with a partner who is, or who is thought to be, HIV positive, a hepatitis B carrier or a hepatitis C carrier;
- they are pregnant or have been pregnant in the last year;
- they have recently visited a malarial area, or if they have visited Central or South America at any time, where the parasite *Trypanosoma cruzi* – responsible for Chagas' disease – is endemic;
- they have had any part of their body pierced in the last year.

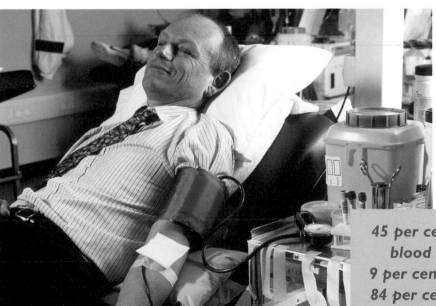

45 per cent of Britons have group O blood and 43 per cent group A; 9 per cent have B and 3 per cent AB; 84 per cent of us are rhesus positive.

GIVING BLOOD

A RADIO ADVERT STATING THAT BLOOD STOCKS WERE LOW HAS PROMPTED CLARE TO GO ALONG TO THE LOCAL BLOOD BANK TO DONATE BLOOD. SHE HAS NOT DONE SO BEFORE.

12.00 SHE ANSWERS A LENGTHY QUESTIONNAIRE ABOUT HER HABITS AND LIFESTYLE, THEN HAS A HAEMOGLOBIN TEST TO CHECK FOR ANAEMIA. THE RESULT IS FINE, SO SHE CAN GIVE BLOOD STRAIGHT AWAY.

12.30 CLARE IS SHOWN TO A BED AND A PRESSURE CUFF IS PLACED AROUND HER UPPER ARM, EXPOSING THE MAJOR VEINS CLOSE TO THE SURFACE OF THE SKIN. THIS AREA IS THEN CLEANED WITH ANTISEPTIC AND A TRAINED VENEPUNCTURIST INSERTS A NEEDLE INTO HER ARM. THE NEEDLE IS ATTACHED TO A COLLECTING BAG.

12.32 CLARE IS ASKED TO CLENCH AND UNCLENCH HER FIST TO ENSURE AN EVEN FLOW OF BLOOD INTO THE COLLECTING BAG WHICH IS JUST UNDER THE BED.

12.40 CLARE HAS BEEN TOLD THAT A FULL DONATION (400–500 ML) WILL TAKE UP TO 10 MINUTES, SO IS UNSURPRISED AT THE WAIT. SAMPLES TAKEN AT THE TIME OF HER DONATION ARE CHECKED FOR INFECTION.

12.45 THE NEEDLE IS REMOVED AND CLARE IS ASKED TO APPLY PRESSURE TO THE NEEDLE SITE TO PREVENT BRUISING. THEN THE AREA IS DRESSED. SHE IS TOLD TO REST AND HAS A CUP OF TEA TO START REPLENISHING THE FLUID SHE HAS LOST.

People in this deferred group will have had a clearly identified episode of risk, but the overall risk of them having an infection that is transmissible by blood transfusion is low. The 12 months act as a period of quarantine, giving time for evidence of infection or a positive test result to appear.

Donors are deferred for a given period if:
- they have had a serious illness or major surgery in the past;
- they are presently on a hospital waiting list or undergoing medical tests;
- they have had recent complicated dental work;
- they are currently on medication;
- they have had contact with an infectious disease, or have recently had certain immunisations.

At a single donor session, about 450–550ml (0.8–1 pint) of blood is taken. The average woman has 4.5 litres (8 pints) of blood and the average man 5.6 litres (10 pints), so no more than 10 per cent of the total blood volume is taken in a donation.

Feeling faint

Some people feel faint after giving blood so it is important to follow all the advice given after the donation. Donors should replenish lost fluid by drinking plenty, but they must avoid alcohol. Smoking should also be avoided as the effects of nicotine will be much stronger after giving blood. It is important not to rush about – however, do not stand or sit still for long periods of time as this can lead to a pooling of blood in the legs. If you do feel faint, bend forward with your head between your knees; when you feel ready to get up move slowly, but if you still feel faint, lie down.

WHAT ARE THE RISKS OF GIVING BLOOD?

Blood donation is very safe and in fact most donors feel better for having given a pint of blood. Donating blood could theoretically make you anaemic, but your haemoglobin level will be carefully checked before each donation.

Some people worry that they can catch infections from donating blood. But the equipment used (needles, tubing) is in sterile condition and will not have been used before. The chances of catching an infection are close to zero.

STORING BLOOD

The risk of transmission of the prion believed to be responsible for variant Creutzfeld-Jakob disease (vCJD) means that the plasma from each blood donation is removed and discarded in donations from the UK. Blood bags have a number of subsidiary bags attached, for preparation of the different blood components.

PLATELETS

Platelets are the smallest of the blood cells, and play an important role in haemostasis, clumping together to form a physical barrier to prevent blood loss. Patients with a low platelet count are prone to bruising and internal bleeding, and in severe cases can literally bleed to death. Most platelet donations are used to prevent bleeding in patients who are temporarily unable to make their own platelets, such as cancer or leukaemia patients, or patients with an autoimmune disease where platelets are destroyed by the patient's own immune system. It is usual for patients to receive so-called

Identical twins are the only people who will have the same antigens on their red blood cells.

'whole blood donations', where platelets from three different donations are pooled into one pack. Patients who require chronic platelet support are given the same number of platelets from just one donor.

THE ABO BLOOD GROUPS

There are a number of systems for identifying different blood groups. The ABO system is the best known, and the most important when it comes to giving blood. Within this system, each person's blood type is determined genetically, and whether you are type A, B, AB or O will depend on the blood types of your parents. In each case, the major differences depend on the presence (or lack) of certain protein molecules in the blood, specifically antigens – found on the surface of the red blood cells – and antibodies found in blood plasma.

ABO incompatibility

Not all blood types are compatible and mixing them can lead to blood clumping or agglutination. Typically a person will develop antibodies to the antigens that are missing. So, if a person has type A antigens on the surface of their red blood cells, they will have B antibodies (anti-B agglutins) in their blood plasma. Should they receive a type-B blood transfusion, the antibodies will start to destroy the transfused red cells, possibly with fatal consequences. This is why group A blood must never be given to a group B person.

BLOOD GROUPS AND PATERNITY

Because of the frequency of the genes in the population, blood groups cannot be used to prove paternity, but it is possible to use them to disprove paternity.
- Two parents who are A can only have a child who is A or O.
- Two parents who are B can only have a child who is B or O.
- An A parent and a B parent can have a child of any group.
- An A and AB, and a B and AB, cannot have an O child. Two O parents can only have an O child. It is possible for two Rhesus positive parents to have a Rhesus negative child, but it is not possible for negative parents to have a positive child. The man, woman and child must all be tested.

Demonstrating the system

The 'tile technique' is used to demonstrate how the system works. The serum from each of blood group A individuals (anti-B), blood group B individuals (anti-A), and blood group O individuals (anti-A and anti-B), is mixed with red cells of unknown ABO blood group. The tile is rocked gently, so the serum and the red cells mix. Clumping (agglutination) of the cells occurs where there is an antibody specific to the antigens on the red cells. Each reaction has a specific pattern – this can be clearly identified by the technician. Where there is no antibody-antigen reaction, the red cells remain in suspension.

WHICH BLOOD TYPES ARE COMPATIBLE?

People with type A blood cannot receive type B blood and vice versa.
Those with blood type O are universal donors as there are no antigens to attack.
AB people are the best receivers, since they have no antibodies to other blood types.

BLOOD GROUP	ANTIGENS	ANTIBODIES	CAN GIVE TO	CAN RECEIVE FROM
AB	A and B	None	AB	AB, A, B, O
A	A	B	A and AB	A and O
B	B	A	B and AB	B and O
O	None	A and B	AB, A, B, O	O

ANTIGENS AND AGGLUTINS

A person's blood plasma contains natural antibodies (agglutins) to A or B, if those antigens are absent from that person's red cells.

BLOOD TYPE	ANTIGENS PRESENT	ANTIBODIES PRESENT
AB	AB	None
A	A	Anti-B
B	B	Anti-A
O	None	Anti-A/anti-B

THE RHESUS SYSTEM

Another significant blood system is the Rhesus system, also discovered by Karl Landsteiner (see page 55) in 1940. The system is named after the Rhesus monkeys on which his experiments were carried out. Regardless of which ABO blood type we have, we will each also be either Rhesus, Rh(D), positive or Rh(D) negative, depending on whether or not the Rhesus antigen is present on the surface of the red blood cells.

A person with Rh(D) positive blood can receive an Rh(D) negative blood transfusion without any problems. However, a person who has Rh(D) negative blood may develop antibodies to Rh(D) positive blood if they come into contact with it. This is of particular significance, and happens most commonly in, childbearing women who are Rh(D) negative, but may be pregnant with a baby who is Rh(D) positive (inherited from the father).

Rhesus disease

Haemolytic disease of the newborn (HDN) is also known as Rhesus disease because most cases within the last 50 years have been associated with Rh(D) incompatibility. In the simplest terms HDN is severe neonatal jaundice of unknown cause in succeeding infants born to the same woman.

How does HDN occur?

It is possible for blood cells of an unborn child to pass into the bloodstream of the mother, usually during the birth process, but also following a termination or miscarriage. Should an Rh(D) negative woman be carrying an Rh(D) positive fetus, a natural rejection process will begin, with the mother producing antibodies to attack the foreign red blood cells. Although a first-born child is at relatively low risk of being affected by this process of immunisation, the risk to an unborn fetus increases with each subsequent pregnancy.

Medication is available to prevent Rhesus disease and it can be given to Rh(D) negative women with Rh(D) positive partners any time there is a chance that fetal cells may enter the pregnant woman's circulation. Used at the right time, the medication is more than 99 per cent effective in the prevention of Rhesus disease. However, it is not effective in preventing the disease worsening once the initial immunisation has taken place.

EATING FOR BLOOD AND IMMUNE HEALTH

Eating well is important in keeping every body system healthy, including the blood circulation and the immune system. A balanced and varied diet promotes general health, keeping the blood healthy and enhancing well-being. Understanding the important nutrients and how to get them into your daily diet is a good first step.

60 *Many vitamins and minerals are involved in the working of the immune system and some foods are believed to improve immune function.*

64 *Delicious drinks and desserts are ideal ways to make sure you get your daily intake of antioxidant fresh fruits.*

65 *Keeping up your red blood cell count is vital for health, but many of us – particularly women – do not always eat enough iron.*

70 *In the last 20 years the vital contribution that folate makes to health – and the effects of too little in the diet – has been recognised.*

72 *Boosting iron and folate intake is not just about eating liver; simple recipes using varied ingredients make healthy eating a pleasure.*

74 *While a little alcohol may be life-enhancing, too much has a serious impact on the blood and immune system.*

Boosting the immune system

Many factors are involved in keeping the immune system working well. Some of these are difficult or impossible for an individual to modify, but both stress and diet are under your control and play a central part in your general health.

The efficient functioning of the immune system is influenced by five main factors:
• genetics
• disease
• drugs
• stress
• diet

The body's resistance to infection relies on the immune system. Many factors are involved in keeping the system healthy, some of which you can do nothing about, such as your genes. The most easily modifiable of these factors are stress and diet.

The most important micronutrient for the immune system is zinc. For example, a recent study in an Indian city showed that providing zinc supplements to slum children improved their immunity to infections. Other nutritional factors are probably less important, but it may be worth boosting your intake of antioxidants and probiotics.

Vitamins and minerals involved in immune function include vitamins C, A, E, B_6, folate and pantothenic acid, essential fatty acids and minerals such as iron, zinc, selenium, calcium, magnesium, manganese and copper. Some of these are also antioxidants – compounds that help to protect your body from damage by free radicals. Free radicals are naturally produced by the body, although sunlight, smoking and pollution can increase their production. There is some evidence that free radicals can damage the immune system, but they also contribute to cancer and arterial disease. If free radicals build up in the body, they can damage our genetic material (DNA), proteins and polyunsaturated fats. Cells in which the DNA has been damaged are more likely to develop cancer.

In addition, free radicals can play a role in the formation of plaque which can build up on the walls of arteries, eventually causing heart disease. Moreover, the development of cataracts, Alzheimer's disease, ageing and inflammation have all been associated with free radical damage. It makes sense for everyone to consume foods and drinks rich in antioxidants to combat free radicals and help protect us from developing diseases of other systems.

The lactose found in fermented milk products like yoghurt is much better tolerated than the lactose found in milk.

PROBIOTICS

Technically a probiotic (from ancient Greek words meaning 'for life') has been defined by experts as 'a live microbial food supplement which beneficially affects the host animal by improving its intestinal microbial balance'. In lay terms, this means if we eat sufficient quantities of beneficial 'live' bacteria, these can alter the balance of existing bacteria in the gut in such a way that the 'good/friendly' types of bacteria suppress the growth of disease-causing 'bad' bacteria, thereby exerting positive effects on health.

HEALTH-BOOSTING *SUPER NUTRIENTS*

Certain vitamins and minerals available in many common foods are particularly beneficial for your general health:

ZINC Found in fortified cereals, seafood and beef, zinc has been proven to boost the immune system.

VITAMIN E Present in seeds, vegetable oils, grains.

CAROTENOIDS Food sources are carrots, melon, red and yellow peppers, mango, spinach, peaches.

MAGNESIUM Found in oysters, shellfish, herring, liver, pulses, milk.

VITAMIN C Sources include all fresh fruits, especially citrus fruits and blackcurrants, and vegetables; fruit juices; many other foods are fortified with vitamin C.

SELENIUM In oily fish, whole grains, egg yolks, cottage cheese, chicken, sunflower seeds, garlic.

BIOFLAVONOIDS Obtained from fruits and vegetables.

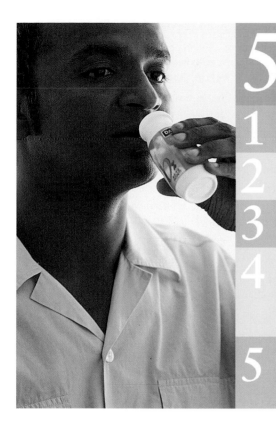

5 Health benefits of lactic acid bacteria

Many people have described the health benefits of lactic acid bacteria, but until recently these claims were anecdotal. However, several studies have now backed up these first findings and research is on-going.

1 IMPROVES LACTOSE ABSORPTION Lactose is a sugar found in milk and dairy products. Before it can be absorbed into the body, it has to be broken down by an enzyme in the gut called lactase. Undigested lactose causes diarrhoea, flatulence and pain.

2 HELPS CONSTIPATION Some studies have shown that among elderly patients, fermented milk products containing lactic acid bacteria help to improve the frequency of bowel movements.

3 PROTECTS AGAINST CANCER Some studies in animals have suggested that lactic acid bacteria inhibit tumour growth, but evidence among humans is limited.

4 LOWERS CHOLESTEROL High levels of low density lipoprotein (LDL) – 'bad' cholesterol – in the blood are a known risk factor for heart disease. Some studies have shown that fermented milk products which contain lactic acid bacteria have the ability to lower LDL cholesterol (but this effect could have been due to the low-fat milk products used, rather than the presence of lactic acid bacteria, as low-fat products have cholesterol lowering properties).

5 IMPROVES IMMUNE FUNCTION Some animal studies have shown that certain types of lactic acid bacteria stimulate immune function, thereby improving protection against infection and cancer. More studies need to be carried out to confirm these findings.

'Friendly' bacteria have been identified as those which make lactic acid: they include strains of Lactobacillus and Bifidobacterium. If these are present in sufficient numbers in the gut they can help to protect us from infection by food-poisoning bacteria such as strains of Salmonella, Shigella, Escherichia and Clostridium. As well as producing substances which neutralise toxins, lactic acid bacteria help to protect against gastrointestinal infections first by lowering the pH environment of the gut, and then by sticking to the surface of the gut wall, preventing food-poisoning bacteria from growing and multiplying there.

Products rich in probiotics are readily available in supermarkets and food stores today. The most common of them are flavoured drinks based on yogurt or soya intended to be taken daily.

Uncertainties of probiotics

- It is unclear whether probiotics have advantages or disadvantages among children under the age of two since the gut is still immature at that age. The effect of changing the balance of the bacteria in the gut is unknown.
- It is also unclear whether there is a potential by some strains of probiotic bacteria to transfer antibiotic resistance.

ECHINACEA

Herbalists believe that this plant, native to America, can boost the immune system, thereby reducing susceptibility to colds and flu, and to treat thrush, middle ear, respiratory and urinary tract infections, and to speed the healing of wounds and inflammation. There is not much evidence from clinical trials to support this thinking.

Echinacea is a member of the daisy family, known by many different names including coneflower, Indian head, Kansas snakeroot, sampson root, comb flower and scurvy root. Three species are used medicinally – *Echinacea angustifolia*, *Echinacea pallida* and *Echinacea purpurea*. Other species may also be effective, but have not been tried.

Echinacea is available as capsules, dried or fresh herbs, liquid extract, ointment, tablets, teas and tinctures. Echinacea is not recommended for children, pregnant women, those with autoimmune conditions or those who are allergic to sunflowers and some other plants such as chrysanthemums. In addition, a course intended to boost the immune system should not last more than four weeks in a row – any longer tends to lead to suppression of the immune system.

GARLIC

Garlic (*Allium sativum*, literally 'all pungent'), is used by herbalists as an anti-inflammatory, an immune system stimulant, and an antiviral and antibacterial agent. It is used to treat colds, flu, infections, heart conditions and high blood pressure, and is also believed to help prevent atherosclerosis. However, clinical trials have not shown any clear-cut benefits for the immune system.

Garlic is generally available fresh and as capsules, liquid extract, oil or tincture. It can cause stomach upsets in some people. While most experts agree that garlic is good for you in normal cooking doses, anyone taking anticoagulants is advised to consult their GP before taking a supplement.

TEA

Tea is rich in flavonoids which act as antioxidants (red wine, nuts, seeds, fruits and vegetables also contain flavonoids). According to a study looking at flavonoid intake and the long-term risk of heart disease and cancer in seven countries, published in 1995, people who had a higher intake of flavonoids (from onions, red wine and apples, in addition to

French scientist Louis Pasteur confirmed the antibacterial action of garlic as long ago as 1858.

tea) had a reduced risk of coronary heart disease. Results from long-term studies conducted in the Netherlands and the United States have also supported these findings.

Not all studies have consistently demonstrated this positive effect on health, however. Of the 13 studies published recently, only four have shown a significant relationship between tea drinking and a decreased risk of coronary heart disease.

A review looking at the effect of tea drinking and cancer risk published in 2000 reported a number of studies in which green tea was associated with a reduction of risk of cancers of the mouth, oesophagus, stomach, colon, rectum, breast and lung among those drinking five or more cups of tea a day. On the other hand, some studies did not suggest a protective effect of tea against cancer. For example, in the study looking at diet and cancer in the Netherlands, consumption of black tea – the sort

Leaf of plenty
Tea has been considered as medicine in China for more than 4000 years. Recent studies seem to bear out that tea – especially green tea – may indeed reduce the risk of developing heart disease.

used for the British cuppa – was not found to affect the risk for stomach, colorectal, lung and breast cancers.

It is difficult to interpret results from human studies since we have to take into account other lifestyle factors besides the diet, such as whether those studied smoked, and their coffee and fat intake. Protective effects could be associated with different lifestyles in different regions of the world. In addition, positive health benefits have mostly been recorded in studies on animals, but the amount of tea drunk by humans is likely to be much less than the doses used to demonstrate disease-preventing effects in a laboratory, so they may not benefit in the same way.

The problem with too much tea

Excessive amounts of tea can interfere with iron absorption from foods such as pulses, cereals and vegetables (tea has no effect on the absorption of iron from meat, poultry or fish) and as such can increase the risk of iron deficiency among vulnerable groups of the population such as infants and toddlers, teenage girls, vegetarians, pregnant women and the elderly. General advice is to allow at least an hour from the end of a meal before drinking any tea to minimise any adverse effects on iron absorption.

Tea is good for you

It is clear that tea is a good source of antioxidants, and provided that we keep levels of tea drinking within the guidelines for overall fluid intake of 6–8 cups a day, tea can make a positive contribution to health. As an alternative, green tea is known to have higher levels of antioxidants and studies have shown that it can help to lower blood pressure.

EATING MORE IMMUNE-BOOSTING NUTRIENTS

For most people, changes to the diet can improve immune function, as well as contributing to overall health. The key is variety: the more foods you include, the more likely you are to get all the nutrients you need. In some cases you need only a small amount of a substance to boost the immune system and remain in optimum health.

- Choose fresh whole foods, organic if possible, and cook them as lightly as you can to preserve all their nutrients. The B vitamins in particular are depleted by cooking.
- Eat a good selection of raw foods which are packed with vitamins and minerals.
- Include lean red meat in the diet, as red meat provides iron, selenium and zinc which are needed to guard against anaemia, as well as helping to heal wounds.

Fruits of plenty
Eat plenty of fruit and vegetables as these will provide antioxidant vitamins A, C, E, folate and phytochemicals, compounds which are important in protecting against the damaging effects of free radicals on the immune system. Include differently coloured fruits and vegetables each day to be sure you fulfil your requirements for different vitamins.

Fish power
Eat more oily fish which provides essential fatty acids. Essential fatty acids derived from the diet are omega 3 or omega 6 fats, and a deficiency – rare in the Western world – compromises immune function. Aim to eat one to two servings of oily fish a week. Vegetables and red meat are also good sources.

Dairy stars
Include low-fat milk and yoghurt in the diet, as these will provide calcium and magnesium. However, try to avoid dairy products with a high fat content as these can increase the risk of arterial disease.

Health-boosting drinks and desserts

An easy and delicious way to boost your health with food is to increase your intake of fruit. The recipes here are all easy to prepare and take advantage of seasonal and more exotic fruits.

SUMMER BERRIES SALAD

500g hulled and halved strawberries
500g raspberries
500g blackberries
250g blackcurrants
250ml elderflower water (made from elderflower cordial and sparkling water)
1 handful chopped mint, to garnish

Place all the fruits in a large bowl, pour over the elderflower water, chill until ready to serve.
Serves 10–12

JASMINE-FLAVOURED DRIED FRUIT COMPOTE

250ml water
1 jasmine teabag
150g dried apricots
150g dried figs
50g dried cranberries
1 small cinnamon stick
peel of half a lemon
1 tbsp orange blossom honey

Bring the water to boil in a pan, add the teabag and simmer for 10 minutes. Remove the bag, add all the other ingredients and simmer for another 15 minutes until the fruit is tender. Remove the cinnamon stick and lemon peel. Serve chilled with reduced fat Greek yoghurt.
Serves 2–3

TROPICAL COOLER

1 ripe papaya, peeled, deseeded, chopped
1 cantaloupe melon, peeled, deseeded, chopped
1 ripe mango, peeled, stoned, chopped
sparkling water

Purée the fruit in a blender until smooth. Thin the purée down by adding a similar quantity of ice cold sparkling water.
Serves 1–2

BERRY SMOOTHIE

125ml grape juice
½ cantaloupe melon, peeled, deseeded and chopped
6 ripe strawberries, chopped
125g pot reduced fat strawberry yoghurt

Blend together and serve ice cold.
Serves 1

Foods for healthy blood

What you eat influences the health of your red blood cells, which transport oxygen around your body. Getting enough iron is important, but so too is understanding what promotes and prevents efficient iron absorption.

Research suggests that people who take regular intense exercise may need 30 per cent more iron than average.

IRON

Iron is a mineral needed for healthy blood. The adult body contains around 4g of iron, half of which is found in our red blood cells as haemoglobin, the red pigment. Some iron is present in myoglobin – the protein found in muscle – and the rest is stored in the body's organs. The primary role of iron as a component of haemoglobin in red blood cells is to transport oxygen from the lungs to the tissues. In addition, iron is required in the make-up of many enzymes which are needed to perform various functions within the body, such as making steroid hormones and detoxifying foreign compounds in the liver.

A lifetime of iron needs

Iron is not excreted from the body in the urine or through the digestive process, it is lost only with cells from the skin and the interior surfaces of the body such as the gut, urinary tract and lungs, and in sweat.

The supply of iron to the fetus is increased during the last three months of pregnancy so that a full-term newborn baby has a total store of around 300mg in its body. This is an important iron store, adequate to cover the baby's needs for the first four to six months – breastmilk is a poor source of the mineral, so the baby does not receive any from this source. After this, the body's iron needs increase rapidly.

Infants who are being introduced to solids need lots of iron. Since they have no iron stores left, their needs at this stage must be met entirely from the diet.

The need for iron increases during adolescence to support the growth spurt for both boys and girls at this time. For women, menstrual losses of iron vary from individual to individual and are mainly genetically determined. The average menstrual loss of iron has been estimated to be around 0.56mg a day. This varies according to the choice of contraception used: the pill, for example, can prevent heavy blood

Daily iron needs

Iron needs vary throughout life, with females needing more than males from puberty until the menopause. Thereafter, needs even out between the sexes.

AGE	IRON (MG)
0–3 months	1.7
4–6 months	4.3
7–9 months	7.8
10–12 months	7.8
1–3 years	6.9
4–6 years	6.1
7–10 years	8.7
11–18 years (boys)	11.3
11–18 years (girls)	14.8
19–50 years (males)	8.7
19–50 years (females)	14.8
50+ years (males and females)	8.7

IRON CONTENT OF FOODS

AVERAGE PORTION	IRON(mg)
One whole stewed pig's kidney (140g)	9.0
140g portion of stewed beef	3.8
100g portion of sardines in tomato sauce	2.9
40g portion of liver pâté	2.4
30g bowl of fortified cornflakes	2.0
Six dried apricots	1.6
50g bar of plain chocolate	1.1
One boiled egg (60g)	1.1
One medium slice of wholemeal bread	1.0
100g portion roast chicken meat	0.7
One medium slice of white bread	0.6
175g portion of boiled potatoes	0.5
20g watercress	0.4
120g fillet of baked cod	0.1
200ml whole milk	0.1

loss while an intrauterine device (IUD) more usually increases menstrual blood loss.

The demand for iron during pregnancy is increased. Although iron absorption does increase in response to need by up to 50 per cent, women with initially low iron stores may be at an increased risk of developing anaemia.

Iron absorption and excretion
There are two forms of iron which are present in foods: haem and non-haem iron. Haem iron is present in meat and meat products such as red meat, liver and other offal meats, poultry and fish. This form of iron makes up around 5–10 per cent of the daily intake in most developed countries. Compared with non-haem iron, haem iron is absorbed relatively well – around 20–30 per cent of the iron you eat is absorbed.

Non-haem iron is found in bread and cereal products (made from fortified white flour), fortified breakfast cereals, green leafy vegetables, pulses, fruits, dried fruit, eggs and dairy products. Up to 95 per cent of our dietary iron is non-haem iron. Unlike haem iron, the absorption of non-haem iron is affected by the status of the body's stores, when these are depleted and when requirements are at their greatest such as in menstruating and pregnant women and growing children, absorption is increased.

Iron deficiencies
In the UK, the average adult daily intake of iron from all sources (foods and mineral supplements) is 14mg for men and 12mg for women. The main sources of iron are:
- cereal products provide 42 per cent of our iron intake;
- meat and meat products yield 23 per cent;
- vegetables contribute 15 per cent.

Enough is enough
Growing children need iron but it is extremely important not to exceed the RNI, as accidentally taking iron tablets is the most common cause of death from poisoning among children in the USA.

IRON STEALERS

Factors that inhibit iron absorption

Phytates and fibre rich foods Phytates are compounds found in cereals, fibre-rich foods (particularly bran, flour and oats), seeds and nuts. The presence of phytates inhibits the absorption of iron and is dose related: even a small amount of phytates have a large effect. Vitamin C in large quantities can counteract the inhibitory effects of phytates.

Tea, coffee, cocoa, spinach and spices These contain compounds called phenols which inhibit iron absorption.

Calcium-rich foods Foods such as milk and cheese can interfere with the absorption of iron from foods. Some studies suggest that one glass of milk reduces the absorption of iron by a half.

These intakes are above the reference nutrient intake (RNI) – the amount that is sufficient to meet the requirements for almost all individuals – for men but below that for women.

A survey looking at the diet of young people aged between 4 and 18 years old found that iron intakes were low in nearly half of girls aged

IRON-FRIENDLY FOODS

Factors that enhance iron absorption

Vitamin C-rich foods Vitamin C enhances the absorption of non-haem iron and is found in fruits, vegetables and juices. Eating a food rich in vitamin C with a meal may double or even triple the amount of iron absorbed.

Meat, fish and seafood The presence of these protein-rich foods in the diet promotes the absorption of non-haem iron (meat also enhances the absorption of haem iron).

Citric acid Fermented vegetables such as sauerkraut and fermented soy sauces contain citric acid which enhances the absorption of non-haem iron.

between 15 and 18. In this group the main sources of iron were:

- fortified breakfast cereals provided around 25 per cent of iron intake;
- vegetables, including potatoes, provided 17 per cent;
- meat contributed 14 per cent;
- bread provided 13 per cent.

Low intakes of iron over a period of time can lead to iron deficiency. Iron deficiency, however, is not the same as iron deficiency anaemia. In iron deficiency, the body's stores of iron are progressively reduced as a result of low levels of iron intake from the diet and/or high menstrual losses. This progresses to anaemia when insufficient iron is delivered to the red cells to make haemoglobin. In contrast, iron deficiency anaemia is defined clinically as having a blood concentration of less than 11.5g/dl in women or 13.5g/dl in men.

Iron deficiency occurs more frequently than iron deficiency anaemia. In developed countries the prevalence of iron deficiency anaemia is up to 8 per cent. The rate for iron deficiency alone, however, is much higher in Western countries – the absence of iron stores is found in up to 30 per cent of women of childbearing age.

Because of children's high requirements to meet tissue growth, young children and adolescents (also because of menstruation in girls) are particularly vulnerable to iron deficiency. Iron deficiency in preschool children and in children from some ethnic groups is common and is linked with late weaning – when solids are introduced late, since breastmilk is a poor source of iron – and the early introduction of cow's milk (cow's milk, too, is a poor source of iron). Researchers have suggested that the lack of halal meat-based weaning foods may

Excessive iron intake over a number of years can lead to health problems including liver disease and cirrhosis.

be responsible for low iron intakes in some children from ethnic minorities.

Mild iron deficiency, without anaemia, is linked to reduced physical performance, mood changes, reduced ability to concentrate and reduced resistance to infection.

In a study of almost 400 middle-class London children aged 12–14, the prevalence of anaemia in the group was found to be 14.5 per cent, with very low iron intakes and low vitamin C intakes. Anaemia was also three times more common among girls than boys – particularly among girls who reported that they had tried to lose weight over the past year (23 per cent) – and among vegetarians (25 per cent). Vegetarianism is common among adolescents: a government survey on young people found that 1 in 10 girls in the 15–18 age group reported they were vegan or vegetarian.

The problem of nutritional anaemia extends to ethnic minority groups in Britain; of 80 Asian girls studied in the 12–15 age group, 16 per cent were anaemic.

For elderly people, the most common cause of iron deficiency anaemia is blood loss due to undiagnosed gastrointestinal bleeding, a symptom of cancer of the colon or stomach.

Symptoms of iron deficiency anaemia include general fatigue, lethargy, giddiness and breathlessness on exertion.

VITAMIN B$_{12}$

Vitamin B$_{12}$ is a water-soluble vitamin which is stored in the liver. Vitamin B$_{12}$ is needed for the manufacture of nerve cells, and is also required by bone marrow cells to make healthy blood.

Vitamin B$_{12}$ deficiency

In the UK, the average adult intake of vitamin B$_{12}$ is 7.3mcg a day for men and 5.4mcg a day for women – both of these are above the reference nutrient intake for adults. This intake is supplied by the diet roughly as follows:

- Half of the vitamin B$_{12}$ we eat comes from meat and meat products.
- Milk and dairy products supply 18 per cent of our B$_{12}$ intake.
- Fish and fish dishes contribute 13 per cent.
- Eggs yield 8 per cent.

A long-term deficiency of vitamin B$_{12}$ can cause irreversible neurological damage. Low levels of vitamin B$_{12}$ in the body can be a result of:

- a poor diet;
- interaction with some types of drugs, such as some antidepressants and antibiotics, and the contraceptive pill;
- interaction with alcohol;
- pernicious anaemia – this prevents the absorption of vitamin B$_{12}$;
- removal of portion of the intestine (commonly for Crohn's disease).

Because vitamin B$_{12}$ is contained exclusively in animal and animal products, vegetarians – particularly vegans – are at increased risk of being deficient. However, deficiency due to inadequate dietary intake is rare, because unlike other water-soluble vitamins, vitamin B$_{12}$ is stored in the liver. Isolated cases of deficiency have been reported in infants breastfed by vegan mothers and in young children on macrobiotic and vegan diets which exclude foods which have been fortified with vitamin B$_{12}$.

Low vitamin B$_{12}$ status is more common in older people and is usually due to malabsorption in the gut. A compound known as 'intrinsic factor' is needed to help transport vitamin B$_{12}$ from the gut to the blood: in some cases, older people have lost the ability to make this factor. In other cases, deficiency is caused by a reduced ability to make the enzyme needed to release vitamin B$_{12}$ from foods. This disease tends to occur among northern Europeans, with a prevalence rate of around 10 per cent after the age of 60.

To ensure they do not become deficient in vitamin B$_{12}$, vegetarians and, particularly, vegans are advised to eat food fortified with the vitamin. These include:

- yeast extract;
- vecon vegetable stock;
- veggieburger mixes;
- textured vegetable protein (TVP);
- soya milks;
- vegetable and sunflower margarines;
- breakfast cereals.

Food labels should indicate those products which have been fortified.

Daily B$_{12}$ needs

Vitamin B12 is found only in animal products and in microorganisms like yeast. Liver is the richest source while eggs, cheese, milk, meat, fish and fortified cereals contain useful amounts.

AGE	B$_{12}$ (MCG)
0–6 months	0.3
7–12 months	0.4
1–3 years	0.5
4–6 years	0.8
7–10 years	1.0
11–18 years (boys and girls)	1.2
19–50+ years (males and females)	1.5

Breastfeeding women need an extra 0.5mcg per day.

VITAMIN B$_{12}$ CONTENT OF FOODS

AVERAGE PORTION	B$_{12}$ (mcg)
100g portion of fried calf's liver	58
120g fillet of baked cod	2.4
200ml whole milk	0.8
One boiled egg (60g)	0.66
30g bowl of cornflakes	0.51
40g cheddar cheese	0.44
10g teaspoon of yeast extract	0.1

COMBATING ANAEMIA

The easiest way to ensure you do not become anaemic is to make sure your diet includes iron-rich foods, and exclude those foods which limit iron absorption. For anyone who becomes anaemic, there are some simple coping strategies which other sufferers have found helpful, while their stores were being rebuilt.

Baby boost *Use an iron-fortified formula while your baby is making the transition from milk to solid foods and do not give babies under a year old cow's milk.*

Clothes comfort *Wear loose-fitting clothes: tight or restrictive clothing impairs your ability to breathe, which will make symptoms of anaemia more acute.*

Take a seat *Sit down whenever you can – don't stand if you can sit. You could even try putting a plastic stool in the shower to sit on while showering.*

Limit tea *Limit the amount of tea you drink: tannins – present in tea and also in red wine – interfere with iron absorption. Avoid tea with meals.*

Iron rules *Eat iron-rich foods: meat, leafy green vegetables, beans, almonds. But remember that although liver is a rich source of iron, it should not be eaten more than once a week since it is also a concentrated source of vitamin A, which can be harmful if eaten in large amounts.*

Foods for health *Increase your intake of folic acid: many breads and cereals are fortified with this mineral which is also present in leafy green vegetables, especially broccoli. Avoid eating calcium-rich foods at main meals but increase your intake at breakfast and as snacks.*

Fruitful combinations *Vitamin C enhances the absorption of both non-haem and haem iron so make sure you include foods and drinks rich in this vitamin – such as fruit, vegetables and fruit juices – with your meals.*

Slow down *Anaemia saps energy. Do what you can physically: this may involve walking or moving more slowly than you are used to – but rest when you feel tired and whenever are able to, so that you conserve your energy.*

Folate and folic acid

Folate has many functions within the body: it is involved in the production of DNA (the material that carries the genetic code responsible for all our cells) and interacts with vitamin B$_{12}$ to make healthy blood cells.

Folate is the naturally occurring form of one of the B vitamins in foods, while folic acid is the synthetic form of the vitamin used in dietary supplements or fortified foods.

FOR WOMAN PLANNING TO CONCEIVE

There is considerable evidence to suggest that folic acid can protect against neural tube defects such as spina bifida and anencephaly if taken in the early months of pregnancy. In neural tube defects, the protective covering of the spinal cord in the fetus fails to develop properly. The protective effects of folic acid are such that the Department of Health recommends that women who intend to conceive and those who are up to three months pregnant should take a 400mcg folic acid supplement a day in addition to their normal requirements from food sources (making a total of 600mcg a day). A woman who has had a pregnancy affected by a neural tube defect is advised to take a daily supplement of 5000mcg (5mg) in addition to the normal requirement from food (a total of 5200mcg, or 5.2mg).

FOLATE-RICH FOODS

Folate is present in small amounts in many different foods. Rich sources of the vitamin include:
- liver and other offal;
- yeast extract;
- green leafy vegetables such as spinach, broccoli and lettuce;
- strawberries and citrus fruits;
- pulses;
- fortified breakfast cereals;
- fortified bread.

Most fruits, meat, milk and dairy products contain very small amounts of folate. Because it is water soluble and heat sensitive, care must be taken when cooking foods rich in folate since at high heat it can readily be destroyed; it is also lost in large amounts of cooking water. For this reason it's best to eat fruit and vegetables raw or lightly steamed whenever possible, and choose cereals that do not require heating.

In the UK, the average adult intake of folate per day is 312mcg for men and 219mcg for women – above the reference nutrient intake (RNI) for both groups. Dietary sources are:
- cereal products provide 21 per cent of our average folate intake;

All steamed up
Folate is fragile and easily lost in too much cooking water and at high temperatures. Steaming foods rich in folate, such as vegetables, can help to preserve this important nutrient.

Folate

The RNI is the average dietary intake level, sufficient to meet the requirements of healthy individuals at each life stage. Most diets meet recommended folate levels.

AGE	FOLATE (MCG) RNI PER DAY
0–12 months	50
1–3 years	70
4–6 years	100
7–10 years	150
11–50+ years	200

Pregnant women need an additional 100mcg a day and breastfeeding mothers require an extra 60mcg a day.

FOLATE CONTENT OF FOODS

FOOD	FOLATE (mcg) per portion
60g black eye beans	126
90g portion of steamed Brussel sprouts	99
30g fortified breakfast cereal	75
85g portion of steamed broccoli	54
175g portion of boiled potatoes	46
70g portion of steamed frozen peas	33
One medium slice of wholemeal bread	14
One medium slice of white bread	10

- vegetables provide 16 per cent of our average folate intake;
- milk, dairy products and meat provide less than 10 per cent of our average daily intake;
- fruit juices contribute around 5 per cent of our daily intake;
- beer can be a rich source of the vitamin, providing up to 16 per cent of the average intake a day in men.

THE PROBLEMS OF TOO LITTLE FOLATE

Deficiency of folate can lead to megaloblastic anaemia, in which red blood cells become much larger than normal. Patients often have a sore tongue, gastrointestinal upsets, anorexia, dyspepsia, constipation or diarrhoea. In addition, the nerve tissues can degenerate and there is often numbness and pins and needles, starting in the feet (these are similar to the symptoms of pernicious anaemia).

Low levels of folate in the body can be a result of:
- a poor diet – folate deficiency is traditionally associated with people on low incomes, and also among elderly people, who often avoid vegetables and fruit claiming that they are 'difficult to eat';
- malabsorption of the vitamin in the gut (in coeliac disease, for example);
- pregnancy, since there is an increased breakdown of folate at this time;
- interaction with some types of drugs, such as anticonvulsants;
- interaction with alcohol, which causes decreased absorption from the gut as well as increased excretion in the urine.

Recent research has shown a relationship between folate intake and the risk of cardiovascular disease. High levels of a compound called homocysteine in the blood is a risk factor for cardiovascular disease, a moderate reduction of folate intake has been found to increase levels of homocysteine. However, trials in which diets are supplemented with folic acid to reduce homocysteine levels, have not yet shown a reduction in cardiovascular disease.

There has been a recent proposal by the government to fortify all wheat flour with folic acid to ensure adequate intakes among groups at risk of deficiency but a decision on this has yet to be finalised. In the USA, wheat, rice, pasta and cornmeal products have been fortified with 140mcg of folic acid per 100g since 1998.

It is estimated that fortifying wheat flour with folic acid could reduce the number of pregnancies affected by neural tube defects by 40 per cent.

71

Recipes for boosting iron and folate

As so many foods are rich in iron or folate it is not difficult to get enough of these essential nutrients from the diet. The recipes here offer some delicious menu ideas.

Foods that contain iron tend to be colourful, since iron salts are pigmented – liver, red meats and leafy green vegetables are good sources, while milk, for example, is not.

BEEFY POTATO SALAD

2 cloves garlic, crushed
4 tbsp tarragon
1 tbsp mustard seeds
1 tbsp fennel seeds
1 tbsp sunflower oil
450g beef tenderloin, trimmed of fat
1 large fennel, sliced thinly
500g new potatoes, halved and boiled until tender
1 red onion, chopped
1 large red pepper, sliced thinly
1 small red chilli, deseeded and sliced
juice of one lime
salt and pepper to taste
handful of chopped fresh coriander

Combine the garlic, spices and oil, rub the mixture over the beef, then leave to marinate for 30 minutes. Preheat the oven to gas mark 7 (220°C/ 425°F). Pan sear the beef over a moderately high heat until brown on all sides, remove and place on a preheated baking tray and roast in the oven for 10 minutes. Reduce the heat to gas mark 5 (190°C/ 375°F) and roast for another 10 minutes for medium done. Remove the beef from the oven and let it stand for 15 minutes before slicing.

Meanwhile, combine the fennel, potatoes, onion and pepper in a serving dish, add the chilli, drizzle over the lime juice, toss to mix, and adjust seasoning if necessary. Arrange the sliced beef over the top. Sprinkle with chopped coriander just before serving.
Serves 4

MIXED GRAIN PILAU

50g quinoa
50g long grain brown rice
50g buckwheat
850ml vegetable stock
1 tbsp olive oil
1 large garlic clove, crushed
2 shallots, peeled and chopped
450g passata
1 tbsp tomato purée
1 bay leaf
2 tbsp fresh oregano
100g French beans
100g frozen peas
2 large artichoke hearts
salt and pepper to taste
juice of one lime
12 mixed green and black olives
1 lime, cut into wedges
handful flat leaf parsley, to garnish

Wash the grains. Bring the stock to boil in a pan, add the quinoa, brown rice and buckwheat, cover and simmer for 30 minutes or until all the stock has been absorbed and the grains are soft.

Meanwhile, heat the oil in another pan and gently fry the garlic and shallots for 5–7 minutes or until soft. Add the passata, tomato purée and herbs and simmer for 20 minutes. Turn the heat up, add the vegetables and cook for 5 minutes. Season and add the lime juice.

Combine the sauce and grains in a large serving bowl, garnish with olives, lime wedges and parsley.
Serves 4

SPINACH SALAD WITH SESAME DRESSING

450g young spinach leaves, washed
60g toasted sesame seeds
1 tsp brown sugar
2 tsp shoyu (low salt soy sauce)
3 tbsp dashi (fish and seaweed broth)

Blanch the spinach leaves in boiling water until they begin to wilt. Drain and set aside in a bowl. Mix the remaining ingredients together to make the dressing and pour on the spinach leaves just before serving.
Serves 4

Alcohol, blood and the immune system

Alcohol is associated with food, socialising and relaxation, and can be one of life's pleasures. In moderation, it may have positive health benefits, but taken in excess it can have serious effects on health.

Excess alcohol dramatically increases the risk of death from liver disease, stomach cancer, pancreatitis and road traffic accidents.

Although less important than these problems, alcohol can also damage the immune system. Some of this damage is related to liver disease, but people who drink excessively are often malnourished: alcohol suppresses the appetite so a drinker may not eat well, and alcohol may inhibit the absorption of nutrients from food. Poor nutrition in turn may damage the immune system. These effects are entirely dose related: the more alcoholic drinks consumed, the more the immune system is compromised. Any quantity of alcohol that results in intoxication is damaging the immune system.

Alcohol also affects red blood cells. It can result in anaemia, with symptoms ranging from fatigue to impaired mental capacity. It also decreases the blood's clotting ability.

ALCOHOL AND NUTRITION

In terms of nutrient content, alcohol is a source of energy, with 1g providing 7kcal or 29kJ. In the UK, the average daily calories derived from alcohol by men is 175kcal (732kJ) compared with 48kcal (200kJ) by women. However, the way in which the body processes and uses energy from alcohol is complex.

ALCOHOL AND CALORIES

All alcohol contains calories. The table below shows the average calorie content of some of the most popular drinks:

ALCOHOLIC DRINK	ENERGY (KCAL)	(KJ)
1 glass of dry white wine	82	344
1 glass of sweet white wine	118	493
1 glass of red wine	85	355
1 pint of beer	184	758
1 pint of lager	167	689
1 small glass of sherry	59	245
1 single measure of spirit	62	257
1 measure of liqueur	64	268

Is Guinness really good for you?

'Guinness is good for you' was coined as an advertising slogan in the 1920s, largely as a result of market testing in which people were asked how they felt after a pint and said they felt good. It is possible that it can be good for you: it is low enough in alcohol to be relaxing but not intoxicating in moderation, it is not especially high in calories, and it may have a slight laxative effect. It also contains iron, which is why traditionally it was given to blood donors and breastfeeding mothers. It is no longer given to blood donors and current advice to women is not to drink alcohol when pregnant or breastfeeding. More stringent advertising standards in many countries mean that the company can no longer make this claim for the product.

ASK THE EXPERT

Studies have shown that when alcohol is substituted for carbohydrates, calorie for calorie, people derive less energy from alcohol than from food.

Beer does contain significant amounts of vitamin B_2 (riboflavin) and niacin, while Guinness and other 'stouts' can be a good source of iron – a pint contains 1.1mg. Spirits do not contain any vitamins.

Anyone who drinks to excess is running major health risks, regardless of any nutritional supplements they may take.

EXERCISING FOR CIRCULATORY HEALTH

Exercise plays an important part in keeping your blood and immune system healthy. Regular exercise strengthens both the heart and the leg muscles so the blood is pumped around the body efficiently. Moderate exercise can also boost the immune system. It is never too late to start exercising, but choose appropriate activities that you will enjoy.

76 *All forms of exercise will improve circulation – by strengthening your heart and keeping your arteries and veins supple.*

78 *A few simple lifestyle changes can help to prevent or ease vein problems. Learn how diet, exercise and even clothing can all help.*

82 *As more people take holidays in mountainous regions it is important to be aware of the problems high altitude can cause.*

84 *Find out how intensive exercise can affect the immune system, and what can be done to prevent overtraining.*

Exercise and circulation

Any form of exercise – vigorous or gentle – will help to boost your circulation. Aerobic exercise promotes cardiovascular health, while regular stretching and flexing can relax tense and stiff muscles, enabling the blood to flow freely.

CARDIOVASCULAR HEALTH

Exercise improves blood circulation by maintaining a strong heart and healthy blood vessels.

A healthy heart

The most important organ to keep the blood flowing is the heart. The heart is a muscle, and like all muscles it becomes stronger and more efficient with regular challenge.

At rest, the average heart pumps about five litres of blood per minute; during exercise this can increase to over 20 litres per minute. The additional effort this requires, strengthens and tones the heart. It is then able to pump more blood with every beat, and increase the level of pumping (if required) with less strain. This lowers the risk of heart attack and other coronary disease.

The best type of exercise for the heart is 'aerobic' – this can include jogging, skipping, cycling or rowing.

Artery and vein wall elasticity

Regular exercise helps to keep blood vessel walls flexible. As soon as exercise begins, nerve and chemical signals stimulate the artery walls to widen, in anticipation of increased blood flow. The increased movement of blood vessel walls during exercise – both expansion and contraction – ensures they remain supple and elastic. This maintains normal blood flow and normal blood pressure. Even a simple form of exercise such as walking can improve the efficiency of blood vessels.

Blood components and pressure

Exercise also helps to maintain good circulation by preventing fatty build-up in the arteries – known as atherosclerosis. This is caused by deposits of cholesterol, fats and proteins on artery walls, which build up and form a 'plaque'. As this plaque hardens and thickens, it significantly reduces blood flow through the artery. If blood pressure is already high, this can increase the risk of heart attack and stroke.

Regular exercise helps to prevent and even reverse atherosclerosis. Firstly, exercise lowers the amount of fat available for deposit, by reducing the amount of harmful cholesterol stored in the body and carried in the blood. Secondly, regular exercise lowers blood pressure. This means that less cholesterol and fats are forced against the artery walls. Blood pressure is further lowered when plaque on the artery walls is swept away by the increased pumping of blood during exercise.

Body temperature

During exercise the body uses its circulatory system to regulate internal temperature. Muscles generate heat during exercise – in response, blood vessels dilate and more blood is pumped closer to the surface of the skin. As it circulates near the surface, heat is released from the body. In the process of preventing dangerous overheating, the body keeps blood vessels healthy and improves circulation.

Exercises for boosting circulation

These exercises will warm you up and help to get the blood flowing if you have become cold or stiff. Try to do exercise of this type every couple of days.

1 FULL BODY SWING Stand with both arms reaching upwards. Swing both arms down past your legs as you bend your knees and curve the body forwards. Then swing the arms and the body upwards again. Perform several swings with real gusto and you will feel the body beginning to warm up and the blood flowing.

2 POINTE WORK Contraction of the leg muscles can help the blood flow in the legs so do these exercises regularly. Stand holding onto a wall or chair for balance. You are going to perform a 4-count movement:
1 – Contract your calf muscles to raise yourself up onto tiptoe. Hold this position. 2 – Bend the legs (whilst keeping your heels lifted). 3 – Lower the heels slowly to the ground whilst

2 **3**

keeping the bend in the legs. 4 – Press the legs straight. Repeat this 4-count move 10 times.

3 FLEX AND POINT Lie on the floor and lift one leg into the air. Rotate the ankle first one way then the other. Now flex the foot (by pulling the top of the foot towards you) and then point it. Do this flex and point several times on each leg.

4 CYCLES Lie on your back and lift both legs in the air, then revolve your legs in circles as if your were on a bike

pedaling backwards. This movement, and the fact that your legs are lifted, will aid the blood flow in the veins. Perform 10 revolutions each night.

5 AIR PRESS Lie on your back once again and this time bend both knees into the chest. Aim to keep your lower back pressed comfortably towards the floor and hands on the floor for support. Now push both legs out, up into the air so that they are straight. Then push the legs forwards at a 45-degree angle so that they are not pushed directly up to the

ceiling and they are not pushed towards the ground, which will put stress on the back. Bend them back in to the start position and repeat 9 more times.

Other exercise ideas
Other good exercise options you may wish to try could include yoga, tai chi, qui gong and walking. If you feel confident, cartwheels and handstands are great for sending the blood flowing to the face and head. Massage and reflexology are also believed to help boost circulation.

4 **5**

Keeping your legs healthy

Several unsightly, painful and potentially serious circulatory conditions have their origins in the legs. Keeping your legs fit and healthy through relatively simple lifestyle changes can pay huge dividends, especially as you age.

VARICOSE VEINS

Varicose veins are the unsightly protrusions of a twisted or bulging blood vessel. These veins are usually blue in appearance and close to the surface of the skin. As they swell with blood they can throb, feel heavy and become uncomfortable. The legs and feet can even swell and the skin may feel itchy. Varicose veins are most common in the back of the calves or on the inside of the legs, yet they can occur in other places such as the rectum (haemorrhoids) in the gullet (oesophageal varices) and in the scrotum (varicoceles).

Causes

As blood returns to the heart after delivering oxygen around the body, the contraction of the calf and thigh muscles compresses the veins and pumps the blood upwards. The veins in the legs have one-way valves to prevent blood from flowing backwards under the force of gravity. If these valves weaken, and the vein walls lose their elasticity, blood collects in the veins causing them to stretch and bulge. Circulation in the legs worsens, which can lead to painful 'heavy' legs from varicose veins and other complications.

What puts you at risk?

Experts agree that the greatest determiner as to whether someone will develop varicose veins is family history. The condition affects 10–20 per cent of the population and over 50 per cent of these people have relatives who have suffered. Women are more affected than men and incidence increases with age.

Lifestyle factors also play a huge part in increasing someone's risk. Obesity, for example, increases the stress placed on the veins. The extra weight presses down on the thigh and leg veins, causing them to weaken. Obesity also means extra fatty tissue, which gives less support to the veins and leads to a loss of tone in the vein walls. Age can also lead to a weakening of the supporting connective tissue.

Prolonged sitting or standing can take their toll, as they increase the pressure on the legs. This is particularly relevant to people working on their feet for long periods – shop assistants for example.

In some women, the enlarged veins can first occur – or worsen – during pregnancy, due to hormonal changes as well as the pressure caused by the growing baby.

A long-standing threat
People who spend much of their working day standing up in the same position, such as hairdressers, are at increased risk of developing varicose veins.

RESTLESS LEG SYNDROME

Restless leg syndrome (RLS) is a non-life threatening, but intensely irritating condition where people suffer from an urge to move their legs. Its sufferers have given this syndrome many different names, but it basically involves unusual sensations in the legs (and sometimes other parts of the body) that make the person move them in order to try to relax them.

The symptoms usually occur more in the evening when the person is attempting to relax. Some people describe the feeling as 'creepie crawlies' or 'burning' up the legs whilst others suffer more jerky or jumpy spasms. In many cases it can disrupt sleep patterns and has been known to cause injury to the person's sleeping partner.

It is not known what causes the condition, although in some cases it may be nerve damage. It is not even known, at this time, where the RLS impulses are generated, although there is some new evidence that points to a linkage of chromosomes 5 and 10. There is also a genetic link. so the condition tends to run in families. The most common sufferers of RLS include middle aged people (the condition gets worse with age), women who are pregnant and individuals under stress. People with poor circulation or anaemia may also suffer.

What can you do to relieve the symptoms of RLS?

- Iron or folic acid supplements can be given to stave off anaemia.
- Good hydration and relaxation techniques may help with stress and tiredness.
- Restricted caffeine intake is recommended. Although caffeine was believed to reduce symptoms, it only delays their intensity.
- A balanced diet (with plenty of fruit, vegetables and carbohydrates, modest amounts of protein and dairy products, and a limited amount of fat and sugar) will help to keep the body's systems healthy.

Bedtime routine
These gentle stretches may help:

1 Lie on your back on the bed and lift one leg straight up towards the ceiling, so that you can feel a stretch in the back of your leg. Then bend the leg in towards you and hold the leg with both hands. Release and extend the leg back to the ceiling. Repeat with the other leg.

2 Raise one leg and gently circle the whole leg, drawing a circle on the ceiling with your foot. Move the leg in a circular motion, slowly mobilising the joint at the hip and thigh. Circle the leg 8 times in one direction and then in the other. Repeat with the other leg.

3 Finally, raise both legs as straight as you can and push your heels towards the ceiling. You will feel a stretch in the back of the legs — the hamstring muscles.

Preventing varicose veins

The best way to avoid varicose veins is to follow guidelines for staying healthy. Keep your weight within the recommended range for your height, and exercise regularly. Exercising will provide regular contractions of the muscles thereby helping the blood flow and circulation.

Try to avoid standing or sitting for long periods of time, but if you have to then regularly lift your heels and flex your feet to contract the calves. Try to take regular breaks where you walk about, to keep the blood flowing. Do not to cross your legs when sitting and watch your posture – sit upright so as not to pressurise certain areas. Practice lifting your legs when lying down and performing some backward cycling movements with the legs.

As a general rule your diet should be low in fat and high in fibre. Some experts suggest a diet rich in bioflavonoids (found in dark green leafy vegetables) and extra vitamin C and E may help. You should drink plenty of fluids (particularly water) so as not to become dehydrated. Likewise, you should restrict your intake of caffeine and alcohol.

If you do suspect you may be susceptible to varicose veins then in addition to the above guidelines opt for loose-fitting garments and wear support tights.

As yet there is no definitive prevention or even cure. The disorder is progressive and whilst sclerotherapy (which seals off small varicose veins) or stripping of larger veins gets rid of the immediate problem, the procedure simply diverts the burden of blood flow to other veins which can, in turn, become varicose.

DEEP VEIN THROMBOSIS (DVT)

A thrombosis is a blood clot in a deep vein. Superficial and deep veins run throughout the body and if a blood clot forms in the valve of a deep vein it can block the whole vein and stop blood flow, causing painful cramps. There is potentially fatal danger if a part of the blood clot breaks away from the main one (the embolus) and travels. If the whole clot travels on in the bloodstream it could block a blood vessel in the lungs or brain, or even the placenta of a growing baby.

DVT was first noticed during World War Two, among people sitting still for hours in air-raid shelters.

What causes DVT?

One of the major risk factors for deep vein thrombosis is staying still for too long. Blood clots can form during a period of just a few hours, if the legs are not exercised.

DVT is often dubbed 'economy class syndrome' because a higher frequency of the problem was noted in travellers sitting in cramped seats. DVT is not restricted to economy class fliers however, or even to long-haul flights. It can affect sales reps or long-distance hauliers, or people who sit for long periods at a desk.

The sitting position can restrict circulation around the legs. The less active the muscles in the leg are, the fewer signals they send to the brain to send sufficient blood to them. The blood that does get to the legs may not circulate as efficiently as normal and clots could develop.

Who is at risk?

People are at higher risk of developing DVT if they:
- are over the age of 40;
- have had blood clots already;
- have a family history of blood clots;
- have cancer or have had treatment for cancer in the past;
- are being treated for heart disease;
- have had recent surgery, particularly on the hips or knees;

DVT is also more common in women who:
- are pregnant;
- have recently had a baby;
- are taking the contraceptive pill;
- are on hormone replacement therapy.

Does aspirin reduce the risk of developing DVT?

There is currently no direct evidence that aspirin reduces the risk of travel-related DVT. However, it is known to make the platelets (part of the blood clotting mechanism) less 'sticky'. If your doctor agrees, take one aspirin a day for three days before your journey. If you are already taking aspirin do not increase your dose. Aspirin should not be seen as a 'quick fix' solution. In a recent study of 1000 airline passengers, some of those who took aspirin still developed blood clots. It appears that aspirin may give a false sense of security, encouraging people to sleep throughout the flight, thereby increasing the risk of DVT.

ASK THE EXPERT

Between 90 and 95 per cent of all people who develop DVT are in one or more of these groups.

People who are overweight, elderly, have to stand in one place for a long time, or have to endure long periods of bed rest may also be at risk. Certain trauma situations and medications can also trigger DVT.

What are the symptoms?

Symptoms may include redness, swelling and heat in the area. There may also be pain, discoloration or ulceration over the area where the vein lies, or joint pain and soreness. Other symptoms may include fever, a rapid heartbeat or a sudden unexplained cough. Sometimes there are no symptoms at all if the thrombus occurs in a vein that is not in the arm or leg.

Treatment

DVT is treated with blood-thinning drugs or anticoagulants. These work by interfering with the body's natural coagulation process, preventing blood from thickening into the semi-solid state that precedes clotting.

Contrary to popular belief, blood thinners don't dissolve clots – the body does. This natural process is called fibrinolysis. Anticoagulants can keep clots from enlarging, however, which is critical. The three types of anticoagulants used to treat DVT are unfractionated heparin (UFH), low molecular weight heparins (LMWH) and warfarin, which is a long-term treatment.

Reducing your risk

An active lifestyle – which includes regular exercise – will keep your body well-conditioned. This is a major factor in preventing DVT.

PREVENTATIVE MEASURES FOR TRAVELLERS

Keeping the blood flowing while sitting for long periods is the important issue. Experts recommend the following when travelling for long periods:

When travelling, make sure you dress in comfortable non-restrictive clothing. Wear comfortable slip-on shoes if possible.

Drink plenty of water before and during the journey to keep well hydrated. Avoid caffeine, alcohol and smoking.

Compression stockings, worn during a journey, have been shown to reduce the risk of DVT.

On a plane get up and walk around every hour. If you can, try to get an aisle seat for extra room to move your legs. If you are a passenger in a car, try propping your feet up on the dashboard or seat in front of you and flexing and extending your feet. If you are the driver, when stationary, work your thigh muscles by lifting your knees up to touch the steering wheel. Then press your feet hard against the floor.

During periods when it is impossible to walk around – if you are required to keep your seat belt on, for instance – place one foot on the other knee and knead and massage the foot and calf using upward motions of the hand, to help circulation. Don't cross your legs at the knee.

Exercise and altitude

High altitude exercise can be great fun but it can also have serious effects for anyone who is unprepared. A few precautionary measures can ensure the enjoyment of high altitude activities such as climbing, skiing, biking or hiking.

The effects of altitude on exercise were first investigated following the 1968 Olympic Games in Mexico City. Here, where the elevation is 2300 metres, for the first time ever there were no world records achieved in events lasting longer than two and a half minutes. The Africans, however, who regularly trained at high altitude, dominated the endurance events.

Now, with more understanding of the effects of altitude on the body's systems, many competing athletes – at all levels – are building altitude adjustments into their pre-competition training.

positive health tips

Getting acclimatised to altitude

Upon arrival you must give your body time to acclimatise. Be aware of any signs of fatigue and reduce your activity levels appropriately.

- Avoid strenuous exercise for the first few days.

- Maintain high fluid (water) intake.

- Increase carbohydrate intake.

- Avoid salty foods and monosodium glutamate (MSG).

- Refrain from smoking.

- Ensure you sleep well. A bath or sauna before bed can help.

It's not just athletes who experience the effects of exercising at high altitude. Increasing numbers of people enjoy skiing, trekking and activity holidays in high altitude regions every year. Unfortunately many people are unaware of how the change in altitude will affect them and do not allow for a period of adjustment. By rushing into activities too quickly, they lose valuable days of their holiday to fatigue or illness.

EXERCISING AT ALTITUDE

When exercising at altitude the main effect on the body is a reduction in cardiovascular capacity: above 1500 metres there is a 10–11 per cent reduction for each 1000 metre ascent. This means that at an altitude of 2000–2500 metres an individual will only be able to perform at 90 per cent of their sea level capacity.

High levels of muscle fatigue are also common, as each lungful of air contains less oxygen, and this oxygen is consumed during exercise.

Such physiological challenges are not serious, and cardiovascular capacity will improve with regular high altitude exercise. It is important, however, for individuals to understand their limitations, and decrease their workload, resistance and pace, particularly upon arrival.

THE BODY'S RESPONSE

At high altitude the air is 'thinner'. This doesn't mean that there is less oxygen (this remains stable at 20.9 per cent) but there is less pressure.

With each breath less oxygen is taken, via the lungs, into the bloodstream and around the body – resulting in a diminished oxygen supply to the muscles and other tissues. This is known as hypoxia.

Hypoxia has wide-ranging symptoms, although most of these are considered to be normal adjustments to altitude conditions. One of the earliest symptoms is impairment of judgement – similar to mild intoxication. Initially this can be felt as a mild headache or slight disorientation. Shortness of breath is another indication of low oxygen levels. The body responds by increasing the ventilation rate (rapid breathing) and cardiac output (faster heart rate) to raise the amount of oxygen available for the tissues. These symptoms usually disappear over 24–48 hours.

ACUTE MOUNTAIN SICKNESS

More serious symptoms of hypoxia indicate the onset of acute mountain sickness (AMS). These include worsening headache, nausea, fatigue, dizziness, acute tunnel vision, slurred speech, staggering walk, memory loss or a combination of these.

AMS is a frequent problem for climbers and it commonly occurs above 3000 metres. It is caused by ascending too high, too fast. The key to managing AMS is to ascend slowly, as acclimatisation takes time. Above 3000 metres the daily ascent rate should be no greater than 300 metres a day. Increasingly, however, factors such as limited holiday time, the increase in the number of high-altitude roads and rapid ascents in cable cars can lead to this basic rule being ignored.

Mild AMS can be treated with rest and a halt in the ascent, plus aspirin or paracetamol to relieve the headache. The symptoms should disappear within 48 hours. Severe AMS should be treated with descent, oxygen and Diamox (the standard drug for altitude sickness which stimulates an increase in breathing).

ACCLIMATISATION

The body adjusts to high altitude by making more red blood cells, to enable more oxygen to be carried in the bloodstream. When the kidneys intially detect the lower level of oxygen in the blood, they release a hormone called erythropoetin. This triggers the bone marrow to start producing more red blood cells within 24–48 hours.

To make room for the increasing number of red blood cells, the body gets rid of fluid from the blood – urine output increases and fluid can collect in the body's tissues. The increase in proportion of red blood cells compared to the plasma (liquid portion) of the blood is called haemoconcentration or 'thick blood'. Initially the body gets rid of 10–15

per cent of the blood's plasma. Full acclimatisation over two weeks would increase a person's red blood cell count by 30–50 per cent.

HIGH ALTITUDE ADVICE

One of the main problems to be aware of at altitude, particularly when exercising, is dehydration. This can be caused by increased breathing and the relatively low humidity of mountainous areas and aeroplane cabins. Sweating while exercising also causes dehydration – as the body cools itself by sweating, 1–2 litres of fluid can be lost per hour. In addition, the increased urinary output caused by the process of haemoconcentration, leads to dehydration. This means that the

blood becomes thicker and blood flow can become more sluggish. Without hydration, unconditioned individuals are at risk of thrombosis.

It is vital to keep well hydrated. Drink regularly during and after exercise, and replace lost fluids with water. Caffeine and alcohol should be avoided if possible as they are diuretics. Avoid salty foods and overeating as these can both magnify the effects of high altitude. Ask for a humidifier in your room as this will increase the water content in the air and relieve dried out sinuses.

Protection from altitude exposure
Ensure you wear clothing designed for altitude conditions. High-factor sunscreen is also recommended as ultra-violet radiation increases by 5 per cent for each 300 metres of altitude.

Getting the balance right

It seems odd, but athletes catch more colds than people in sedentary occupations. Why is this? To understand we need to look in detail at the effects exercise can have on the immune system.

Studies have shown that many high-performance athletes can have chronically lowered immune systems. Indeed, it could be said that in immunological terms, at particular points in their training and competition schedules elite athletes are extremely unhealthy. Many athletes report significant bouts of upper respiratory tract infections (URTIs), which include the common cold, acute sore throat, laryngitis, bronchitis, ear infection and the flu.

During both the winter and summer Olympic Games, clinicians report that URTIs are the most frequent and irksome health problems athletes experience – they affect performance and can jeopardise years of training.

It appears that the main factor which determines the condition of the immune system is the intensity and duration of the exercise.

MODERATE EXERCISE BOOSTS IMMUNITY

Regular, moderate exercise has been shown to stimulate immune function. Positive immune changes take place during each bout of moderate activity. The numbers and activity of natural killer cells increase and T cell function improves. There is also increased blood flow and movement of blood cells.

Although the immune system returns to pre-exercise levels very quickly after the exercise session is over, each session represents a boost that translates into fewer days of sickness and appears to reduce the risk of infection over the long term. Studies show that 60–90 per cent of people who exercise regularly experience fewer URTIs than those who don't exercise.

IMMUNOSUPPRESSION

While regular moderate exercise leads to fewer URTIs, evidence sugests that intense training and competition actually suppress some aspects of the immune response.

Initially, intensive exercise causes a stimulation of the immune system, but for 3–72 hours after exercise, there is a general impairment of the immune system which leaves athletes vulnerable to infection.

Stress response

The body perceives high-intensity exercise as stressful and responds by releasing the stress hormones adrenaline and cortisol into the bloodstream. It appears that it is the fluctuating levels of these hormones which cause many of the immune system changes.

During intense exercise there is a rise in granulocytes (monocytes and neutrophils) and lymphocytes. Among the lymphocytes – which include T cells, B cells and natural killer (NK) cells – NK cells increase the most during exercise. However, these levels fall within five minutes of the exercise ending, and within 30–60 minutes there is a dramatic

Energy needs on the run
Athletes should think about their energy needs on an hour-by-hour basis, not just from day to day. Drinking carbohydrate sports drinks during a long-distance race can help to maintain steady blood sugar levels.

reduction in both the number and activity of lymphocytes. In particular, NK cells plummet to levels 25–30 per cent lower than pre-exercise – a direct result of the cortisol released into the bloodstream. NK activity remains low for 3–6 hours after intense exercise. In addition, the cortisol released during intense exercise causes a decrease in the plasma levels of glutamine, which T cell lymphocytes depend on for optimal growth, so their function is diminished. Intense exercise also causes an increase in free radicals, which cause damage to immune cells.

'Open window'

The cumulative effect of these immunological changes results in a less effective defence system. This is why scientists speak of an 'open window' theory, which highlights a post-exercise period in which athletes are vulnerable. In the 3–72 hours that immunity is lowered, bacteria and viruses gain a foothold, increasing the risk of infection, especially URTIs.

> *Alberto Salazar caught 12 colds in 12 months of training before winning gold in the 1984 Olympic marathon.*

One of the largest studies to date was carried out in 1987, when 2311 participants in the Los Angeles marathon were followed for two months before and one month after the race. Runners who actually ran were compared with those who had signed up but did not run for reasons other than illness. The researchers found that one in seven runners

10-18 YEARS

Overtraining and teenagers

It is especially important for children and adolescents to avoid the risks of high-intensity training.

- **Overuse injuries** Excessive stress or overload can lead to tissue breakdown and injury. Typical overuse injuries are repetitive stress injuries, injuries to developing joint surfaces, and/or injuries to the developing spine.
- **Sexual maturation** Athletic girls tend to experience their first period later or find their periods stop (amenorrhea), due to training stress and low levels of body fat. Training has no adverse effect on male maturation.

- **Nutrition** For young athletes a healthy diet is critical. An iron deficiency can lead to 'sports anaemia', while a calcium deficiency can lead to increased bone fractures. Eating disorders are a risk for female athletes, particularly in sports where low body weight is deemed 'ideal'.

To train without overtraining:
- Avoid excessive training.
- Take scheduled rest periods.
- All training should include conditioning and flexibility.
- Experiment with different sports.
- Watch for warning signs of overtraining and 'burnout'.

developed a cold in the week after the marathon, which was six times the non-runner rate.

OVERTRAINING

Exercising every day for an hour or more at 85 per cent of your maximum heart rate can be considered overtraining. This can lead to a range of symptoms including recurrent URTIs, general fatigue, slow recovery, irritability, depression, poor concentration and sleep disturbance.

To check if you are overtraining, you could try the Rusko test. Lie quietly for 10 minutes at the same time every day and monitor your heart rate – this should stay constant for each 10-minute period. Then stand up and check your heart rate exactly 15 seconds after standing, and then obtain your average heart

rate during the period 90–120 seconds after standing. If you are on the verge of overtraining your standing rate will start to increase over a period of a few weeks. This will give you a chance to ease back on the training.

SENSIBLE GUIDELINES

- Ensure you get plenty of rest to enable your body to adapt to intense training.
- Try to avoid contact with people who have colds.
- Warm up well and keep warm during competitions.
- Take vitamin supplements (vitamin C and zinc) for cold symptoms.
- If you have a cold, reduce training for 1–2 weeks. If you have flu or bronchitis, stop training for 3–4 weeks to prevent damage to your heart – this can be life-threatening.

Frequency:
Whether your goal is to control weight or to get in shape, the frequency should be 3–5 times a week.

Intensity:
Exercise should make you feel energised, not exhausted. Increase intensity slowly – start by walking longer or faster.

Time:
Try about 30 minutes of exercise each session. Daily activities such as walking, gardening and climbing stairs all count.

Type:
The more different types of exercise you do the better. Moderate exercise involving rhythmic leg movements is best.

THE FITT PRINCIPLE

It is not just a question of how often and how long you exercise but also how hard and what type – termed the FITT principle: Frequency, Intensity, Time and Type.

Frequency

Experts say that cardiovascular exercise should be done at a frequency of 3–5 days a week. This may seem difficult, but it doesn't mean you have to go to the gym each time. It can include daily activities such as gardening, walking, cleaning and climbing stairs. Obviously, attending appropriate fitness classes helps too. Beginners should start on three days a week, skipping a day between each session.

Intensity

Start with some endurance based activity like walking and gradually build up towards more vigorous exercise. Increase the intensity slowly, and never exercise to exhaustion. You can measure the intensity at which you are exercising in a number of ways:

- Your cardiovascular level may be gauged by your ability to hold a conversation while exercising.
- Check your heart rate at intervals: it should be no more than 80 per cent of your maximum heart rate (220 minus your age).
- Use self-perception to gauge how hard you are working on a scale of 1–16, where 1 is easy and 16 is extremely hard.

Time

The duration of the aerobic portion of an exercise session should be between 12 and 60 minutes. The less fit you are, the shorter the duration and the more frequently you should exercise. As you become fitter, you can exercise for longer, less often.

Type

A useful approach is to try as many different types of activity as possible. Your body will be less likely to become accustomed to any one type. Trying different exercises also lessens the chances of overuse of any one body part. In addition you are less likely to get bored.

The positive effects of exercise

Regular exercise is good for you. It makes you stronger, it gives you better endurance and gives you more energy. It also provides you with increased self-confidence and enhances concentration.

Exercise promotes an increase in 'good' cholesterol and lowers blood pressure, thereby decreasing the risk of heart attack and stroke. Regular exercise makes you more relaxed and this can boost your immune system; it also has been credited with lowering certain cancer rates.

PROTECTING YOURSELF

The immune system is under daily threat from infections. In addition to building the system up through lifestyle factors such as diet, there are two major ways in which you can support it: vaccination is available against many diseases, and you can avoid behaviours that might compromise the system.

 Since the first vaccination was carried out more than 200 years ago, the process has become a first line of defence against disease.

 Understanding the risks of infection in life is an important first step in helping the immune system to work effectively.

Why vaccination matters

The process of vaccination is one of the greatest success stories of modern medicine, offering the best defence against an expanding range of deadly diseases by giving treatments months, even years, before they are likely to be contracted.

Smallpox vaccination has brought about the complete eradication of the disease's deadly microbes from the environment. The World Health Organization (WHO) is currently targeting further diseases – including polio – for similar treatment, in the hope that several other deadly diseases will be eliminated as a result. Yet, despite such global

Raising healthy kids
The infant death rate has fallen steadily in the last 50 years in the UK, to its current rate of 7 in 1000. Vaccination has played a major part in this success.

success, as well as regional population-based improvements – for example, the virtual eradication of infections due to Haemophilus influenzae type b meningitis in those countries that are now using the Hib vaccine – safety concerns have prompted many people to question the value of immunisation.

THE DANGER OF SCEPTICISM
The process of immunisation involves taking a treatment long before a disease is contracted, often in the knowledge that an individual's risk of contracting the disease is low.

As such, the process requires a strong belief that it will generally do more good than harm. It is important that up-to-date information is available on the balance of risks and benefits, as circumstances can change each year.

A single dose of the MMR vaccine for measles, mumps and rubella will offer approximately 90 per cent of vaccinated children complete protection against measles. However, if only 92 per cent of children – rather than 100 per cent – receive the vaccine (this is the highest uptake rate achieved in the UK), only 83 per cent of all children are protected.

Despite a good vaccine and impressive uptake, therefore, sufficient numbers of children remain unprotected to allow epidemics to develop. Should the number of vaccinated children fall further, the situation becomes worse, changing the overall risk-to-benefit ratio and increasing the need for immunisation.

Since these infections have become rarer, many of us have forgotten how dangerous they are; measles is a killer, mumps can cause sterility and rubella causes birth defects.

At the other end of the scale is polio, which has been largely removed from some parts of the world, including the Americas and Europe, through vaccination. As a result, even though the risk of giving a child the vaccine is very low, the risk of contracting the disease in some areas may be even lower.

Custom vaccination

We know that vaccinations are very low risk because such treatments are among the most commonly administered in the world, and give us more data about their effects than almost any other type of treatment. However, a 'one injection fits all' policy will, inevitably, not fit all or, therefore, protect all. Developments in the science of human genetics may lead to a more personalised process. In the future, genetic testing may indicate which people are more likely to suffer from a particular adverse reaction and who will require more booster inoculations in order to be protected. In addition to this, new vaccines are constantly being developed, and this may make immunisation more important as the number of diseases they are able to combat increases.

IMMUNISING CHILDREN

During the first six months of life we are usually protected from many common diseases by antibodies that

In 1967 when the WHO launched its eradication initiative, smallpox affected 15 million people annually; by 1980 the disease had been eliminated worldwide.

have been passed on to us from our mothers. This gives babies a brief period of time to build up strength before they face the serious challenge of infectious disease, which in some parts of the world kills as many as one in six of the under-fives. Fortunately, this six-month period can now be used to immunise children so that, as their mother's antibodies become less potent, they get additional help in combating infections when they meet them, greatly increasing their chance of surviving their first year.

Currently, immunisations that are available for use during this period protect against diphtheria, tetanus, whooping cough (pertussis) – all in one vaccine called DTP – polio, meningitis group C and haemophilus. In addition, immunisations against tuberculosis (TB), hepatitis B, chickenpox (varicella), and meningitis group A, may be given if the risks are thought to be high enough. 'High risk' is usually defined as:
- close contact with somebody known to be suffering from active disease (typically the mother in the case of varicella);
- living in (or visiting) a country – or simply a city or area – where there is a high prevalence of the specific disease.

Milestones
IN MEDICINE

Edward Jenner had been an English country doctor for 24 years when he first tested his ideas on immunisation. At the time, smallpox was the biggest killer disease, with 10 per cent of the UK population dying from it each year. In 1796, intrigued by stories that people who caught cowpox from their herd did not contract smallpox – even if several other family members caught the disease – Jenner took the pus from a milkmaid with cowpox and put it into cuts made into an eight-year-old boy's arm. The boy suffered what appeared to be a normal, mild, cowpox infection. A few weeks later Jenner risked being accused of murder and repeated the experiment, using smallpox pus. The boy remained healthy and the concept of immunisation was born.

At 12 months it is possible to protect against mumps, measles and rubella using the MMR vaccine.

For those at high risk, the pneumococcal vaccine can be given to children over two years old and the typhoid vaccine above the age of six. Vaccination against yellow fever is also possible.

Adult immunisation programmes are essentially the same as those for children, and most adults can be inoculated to 'catch up' at virtually any age.

Does homeopathic immunisation work?

Scare stories in the media regarding the potential side effects of vaccination have led to a rise in interest in homeopathic alternatives to immunisation. Although such alternatives exist, the Council of the Faculty of Homeopathy only offers treatment to help the body deal with a routine inoculation or in those cases where conventional treatment is not possible. Whether the homeopathic remedies work or not, or have any side effects, is not known because no real scientific studies have been undertaken. The Council of the Faculty of Homeopathy supports the current UK immunisation policy.

ASK THE EXPERT

TRAVELLING THE WORLD

Guidelines for vaccines required for travelling vary depending on where you are going, so a clear plan of destinations is essential. A detailed list will be available at your local immunisation centre. Typical vaccine options are meningococcal ACWY or AC, Japanese encephalitis, rabies, tick-borne encephalitis, typhoid, hepatitis A and B and yellow fever. Yellow fever is now the only disease for which an international vaccination certificate may be required for entry into a country, following travel from a country where it is endemic. This also used to be the case with cholera, but the

legislation has now been dropped because the World Health Organization (WHO) has accepted that the vaccine was not effective at preventing transfer of the infection from one country to another. This vaccine is no longer recommended for any traveller.

In theory each individual travel vaccine should be given its own 10-day period to take effect. In practice, however, owing to time constraints, many vaccines can be given at the same time without apparent adverse effects. Courses of most travel vaccines, plus any single dose vaccines, can be administered over a four-week period. Final doses should be completed before the departure

date to allow immunity to develop. It can take up to four weeks, for example, for full immunity to develop following a Japanese encephalitis vaccination and should anyway be given at least two weeks before departure in case a delayed allergic reaction occurs. A GP or travel clinic can offer good advice on an immunisation schedule.

If children are travelling, many vaccines can be given earlier than the standard schedule (and often from

birth) but it must be remembered that if this is done they may require additional boosters later in life as the immunity from early immunisation does not seem to be as long lasting.

On returning from the tropics it is advisable to visit your GP, even if you are feeling well. It may be that a disease can be detected (for example in a stool sample) before symptoms develop, allowing for more effective treatment.

Mosquitoes can bite through thin material, so spray clothes with permethrin (which may last up to two weeks).

In the evenings wear long-sleeved shirts and long trousers, protect exposed skin with a repellent containing diethyltoluamide (DEET) and wear DEET-soaked ankle and wristbands. DEET preparations are usually only effective for two hours so frequent application is required. Be careful when applying to the face as it can irritate mucus membranes (do a skin test first).

When a bedroom cannot be made safe from insects, use a permethrin-impregnated bed net (which is much more effective than an ordinary net).

For diseases where there is no effective vaccine, such as malaria and HIV/AIDS, a more involved protection programme is required. In the case of malaria, this means visiting your doctor before and after travel, taking the right anti-malaria tablets, and protecting yourself from mosquito bites. Protection against HIV includes behaviour changes – using barrier contraceptives and perhaps chemical prophylactics.

Sleep in air-conditioned or screened accommodation. Rooms should be sprayed with a knockdown insecticide each evening after sundown to eliminate mosquitoes which may have entered during the day.

Avoiding risky behaviours

One of the biggest threats to the immune system is HIV, which can – but need not – slowly break it down. There is a lot an individual can do to reduce the risk of getting HIV or of passing it on, and to stay healthy even after a diagnosis.

HIV is the human immunodeficiency virus. The virus can, but does not always, lead to AIDS – acquired immune deficiency syndrome. AIDS is not a single disease but a collection of the most common illnesses which characteristically affect people living with HIV.

In the UK there are estimated to be around 40,000 people living with HIV; estimates suggest that about one third of these people do not know that they have the virus. There has been a lot of misunderstanding about HIV transmission, as well as misinformation about who is at risk and who isn't.

HIV is passed on in three main ways:
• Through unprotected penetrative sex (anal or vaginal) between someone who is HIV positive and someone who is HIV negative.
• By getting HIV-infected blood into the bloodstream: this can happen when someone who is HIV positive and someone who is HIV negative share needles when injecting drugs. It does not happen any more through blood transfusions.
• A woman can pass the virus to her unborn baby during childbirth.

HIV does not discriminate on the grounds of age, sex, gender, class, race or sexuality. It is an individual's behaviour – and the behaviour of an individual's partner – that puts that individual at risk.

For transmission to take place sexually, there must be a partner who has the virus and a partner who does not, and a route of transmission out of one body and into the other. HIV doesn't emerge as a result of having sex, so unprotected sex between two people who do not have the virus cannot magically produce it, as some people think.

Many people are unaware of the dangers of risky behaviour, and this ignorance is directly affecting the rate at which HIV is spreading, particularly amongst heterosexual people in the UK.

TRANSMISSION AND ORAL SEX

There have been a handful of cases of transmission through oral sex worldwide, but these should be put within the context of how much oral sex is going on. It seems that some very specific conditions have to be in place for oral sex to be a transmission route for infection. Bleeding gums, cuts or sores in the mouth, and inflammation caused by common throat infections, allergies or sexually transmitted infections such as gonorrhoea, are likely to aid transmission. Again, there must be a route of transmission of the virus from a partner with HIV to a partner without HIV. It seems that vaginal and anal sex are more likely transmission routes.

OTHER RISKY BEHAVIOURS

Injecting intravenous drugs is a bad idea for many reasons, but it is vital that users do not share needles. The risk of HIV – and hepatitis – being

HIV AND TATTOOS

HIV is actually a delicate virus which cannot survive long outside the human body. It is usually only transmitted when enough infected blood is introduced into a body. The structure of tattoo needles makes HIV transmission by this route unlikely. It seems that there has never been a case of transmission in this way in the USA, and in cases reported elsewhere the affected individuals were deemed 'high risk' for contracting the virus, whether they had a tattoo done or not.

The main risk when getting a tattoo is infection with hepatitis, a hardy virus that can survive for long periods outside the human body and can be transmitted by an infected needle. Reputable tattooists:
• sterilise all equipment thoroughly;
• use new needles for each client;
• use individual portions of ink and lubricant;
• dispose of used needles following health department guidelines;
• clean couches between clients.

Sex and relationships

TALKING POINT

The desire to have a sexual relationship is a basic human instinct, which does not change after a diagnosis of HIV. But it is important to protect yourself, and your partner, if you have HIV. It is vital that you are protected from other sexually transmitted diseases, as these are more serious for someone with HIV and harder to treat. They can also speed the rate at which HIV damages the immune system. It is also believed that it is possible to be reinfected with a more aggressive or drug-resistant strain of the HIV virus. Whether to tell a prospective partner of a diagnosis of HIV is a personal decision, but partners should be protected from infection. Condoms are widely available and should be carried and used by anyone who is sexually active.

transmitted in this way is high. In some areas needle exchange programmes have been introduced with the aims of ensuring that users have access to sterile needles; that they have access to medical staff; and that there is also social and psychological support available if they want to stop taking the drugs. Where such schemes have been set up, studies indicate that HIV infection rates appear to be falling.

THE BODY AND HIV

HIV works differently from a lot of other infections. It doesn't just try to get into the body and do some damage, it actually finds and attacks the CD4 cells (helper T cells) which are the 'organisers' of the immune system. When HIV moves into an individual's CD4 cells and kills some of them off, the immune system stops working as well as it should. When HIV first gets into the body, a person may get a sore throat, fever or a rash, although the vast majority of patients have no symptoms when

HIV prevention

In 2000, for the first time in the UK more people contracted HIV through heterosexual rather than homosexual activity. However, the spread of HIV is preventable with safer sex (using condoms) and increased HIV testing.

they are first infected. Although HIV attacks the immune system, the body does make antibodies against the virus. These antibodies are present from a few weeks after infection first takes place. The HIV test consists of checking the presence of these antibodies and is very nearly 100 per cent reliable.

Having a test

There is one very good reason to have a test if you suspect that you may have been infected: if you know you have HIV, you can then do something about it. There is no cure for HIV and there is still a lot of prejudice attached to those people living with the virus, so having a test is a difficult decision for many people to make. On the other hand,

it can prevent unnecessary worrying, and many people find that, once they know for sure, they have some relief. Before you have a test, you should be offered pre-test counselling to make sure you completely understand the consequences of testing. You must be asked permission for the test to be done: it can never be done without your consent. There is enormous support from charities offering counselling and basic information on social issues as well as on legal and financial matters (see page 160).

IT'S NOT TRUE!

The myths surrounding HIV

Contrary to popular belief, HIV is quite a fragile virus that is not easily passed on. Here are three common myths on HIV infection:

'You can get HIV from a mosquito bite'

No you can't. Even though these insects suck blood, if the virus enters the mosquito the insect does not become infected and will not regurgitate blood containing HIV into the bodies of other people.

'HIV can spread in a car crash'

There has only ever been one recorded case of HIV infection through a car accident. Blood splash transmission is extremely unlikely in any circumstances. For HIV to be passed on in a car crash, there would have to be cuts or lacerations in both people and sustained contact would have to be made – in other words an entry and exit route for the virus. The chances of this occurring are extremely rare.

'You can catch HIV having your ears pierced or getting a tattoo'

Not if you use a reputable piercer or tattooist who follows standard procedures for sterilising equipment. The perceived risk is that needles that have been used on other people will be reused without proper sterilisation, but no reputable business operates in this way. Ask a prospective piercer or tattooist if you can see their set-up for sterilisation: a good artist will be only too pleased to show you.

STAYING HEALTHY WITH HIV

The fact that someone has HIV does not mean that they are inevitably going to go on to develop AIDS. For a long time the body may still have enough CD4 cells to organise fighting off infections. However, over time, as this number falls, there is a greater chance of picking up infections and the body not being able to deal with them. It is these opportunistic infections which can cause people to become seriously ill and in some cases die, not the HIV itself.

HOW DRUGS CAN HELP THE IMMUNE SYSTEM

Combination therapy (or highly active anti-retroviral therapy) is now widely available for people with HIV in the UK, as a way of combating the virus. Combination therapy consists of different drugs (usually a cocktail of three or four drugs) which is taken each day in order to start to combat the virus and preserve the number of CD4 cells which have survived the attack. These drugs are usually taken for the rest of a patient's life. This is a major undertaking that needs careful consideration. In rare cases it may be possible to take a carefully scheduled short break from the drug regime (a structured treatment interruption). But the long term effects of this are unknown.

Side effects

Some of the drugs have unpleasant side effects, and for this reason can be difficult to take. Nonetheless, it's important to take all the drugs prescribed, even if they produce feelings of nausea or fatigue.

Drug resistance

HIV is a resilient virus – it can quickly make new copies of itself and become stronger. However, as it reproduces it often makes mistakes – so each new generation, or strain, of HIV can differ from one before. This is why it is necessary to keep taking anti-retroviral drugs once a course has been started, to prevent the HIV from making potentially drug-resistant copies.

Anti-retroviral drug resistance can be avoided if the following guidelines are adhered to:

• At least three or four drugs should be taken in combination, as advised by the clinic. If the combination is strong the HIV virus is not able to mutate.
• The drugs must be taken exactly as prescribed. Missing doses, or not taking them on time, lowers the amount of drug in the body so

the virus is not properly suppressed – it can reproduce faster and the risk of resistance increases.

- Regular viral load tests and CD4 count tests will indicate any growing drug resistance.

If resistance does develop, this usually means that the drug regime needs to be changed.

Do anti-retrovirals work?

Since it was introduced in the 1990s, combination therapy with anti-retroviral drugs has helped many people with HIV. However, the drugs which suppress the HIV virus do not eliminate the virus completely from the body. Even when the levels of the virus are almost undetectable, HIV is still there and ready to replicate given the slightest chance.

It is likely that new treatments will develop from current research based on blocking proteins or enzymes found on the HIV virus, in order to prevent HIV replication and spread.

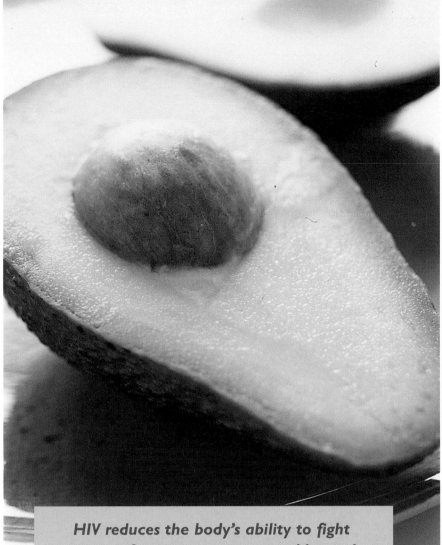

HIV reduces the body's ability to fight minor infections, so raw vegetables and fruit must be peeled or cleaned to remove hidden bacteria and germs.

Are healthcare workers at risk of HIV?

The risk of healthcare workers contracting HIV at work is low, as long as they follow safety guidelines. Casual contact with an individual infected with HIV does not expose anyone – including healthcare workers – to contracting HIV. The main risk of transmission is an accidental injury from an infected needle, but this is extremely rare – scientists estimate the risk at less than 1 per cent.

ASK THE EXPERT

WHAT CAN BE DONE TO HELP THE IMMUNE SYSTEM?

When someone is ill, they are often told to eat well, drink plenty of water and get plenty of sleep. All of these things help the body to fight infections, and it's the same with HIV.

- Get plenty of sleep: when the body is fatigued it must work hard just to keep going and doesn't have time to fight infections.
- Eat a good well-balanced diet. It's important to maintain a healthy weight, which may be difficult if drugs are causing sickness. Nutrient-dense foods such as protein and carbohydrate, as well as plenty of fruit and vegetables, are recommended. Eating little and often can help if eating is a problem.
- Take regular exercise: again this can be difficult when someone is not feeling well, but exercise keeps muscles toned and improves digestion. It can also lift mood and promote good sleep.
- Managing stress will help too. Getting too stressed can affect how the body deals with infections and how well the immune system works.
- Guard against minor infections.

3

What happens when things go wrong

Knowing what can go wrong

The prime causes of problems concerning the blood and immune system are infection, cancer, and genetic and hereditary factors. Another important consideration is the effect on the immune system of drugs prescribed for other illnesses.

INFECTION

Infections are a big problem when the immune system is not working well – when someone has an immune deficiency. Individuals with a weakened immune system are at higher risk of becoming infected rather more often and more severely than they would be if their immune system was working normally. Bacteria and viruses that do not usually cause problems at all can result in so-called opportunist infections, which can be life-threatening. Whatever the cause of the damage to the immune system, a patient may need treatment to prevent these opportunist infections.

Infections can cause damage to the blood and immune system. For example, the Epstein-Barr virus not only causes glandular fever (see page 147), but may also lead to lymphoma in a very few individuals. The HIV viral infection (see page 144) is well known for causing AIDS (acquired immune deficiency syndrome).

CANCER

Abnormal cells of the blood and immune system can cause cancers, such as leukaemias, which affect the white blood cells. These cancers tend to act rather differently from those affecting other organs, which usually start by forming lumps in just one part of the body and then spread to other parts. Instead, they are spread around the body by the blood from the very beginning of the disease. This may sound like very bad news, but it does mean that leukaemia, for example, can be diagnosed very quickly and therefore treatment can be very effective.

PHYSICAL INJURY – TRAUMA

The most common type of injury to affect the blood circulatory system is severe bleeding or haemorrhage. Luckily, blood has evolved an effective clotting system, and in any case the body can usually replace blood that it has lost through bleeding. Because the blood and immune system extends throughout the body, it is not vulnerable to injury in the same way as, say, an arm or a leg. An exception to this is damage to the spleen. This rather delicate organ lying in the upper left-hand side of the abdomen is relatively often damaged by accidents affecting the abdomen and, being difficult to repair, must sometimes be removed (see page 132).

The most famous carrier of an inherited blood disorder was Queen Victoria, who transmitted haemophilia to several European royal families.

POOR NUTRITION AND OTHER DIETARY PROBLEMS

Lack of nutrients can cause blood and immune system damage. For example, a diet that does not contain very much iron or folic acid can lead to anaemia. These nutrients may be lacking in a vegetarian diet, but more often the nutrients are present in the diet at the correct

MORE COMMON

ANAEMIA	LYMPHOMA	HIV (HUMAN IMMUNODEFICIENCY VIRUS)	LEUKAEMIA (ALL VARIETIES)
20,000 PER 100,000 (1 IN 5)	11 PER 100,000 (1 IN 9090)	6.6 PER 100,000 (1 IN 15,000)	5 PER 100,000 (1 IN 20,000)
Estimates suggest that between 10 and 20 per cent of women of childbearing age are anaemic in the developed world; iron deficiency is the most common nutritional mineral deficiency in the UK.	Also commonly known as non-Hodgkin's lymphoma.	In 2001, the number of people diagnosed as HIV positive in the UK exceeded 4000 for the first time.	ACUTE LEUKAEMIAS ONLY
			4 PER 100,000 (1 IN 25,000)
			The incidence of acute leukaemias is highest in young children and older people (aged over 65).

levels, but problems arise because the body cannot absorb enough to maintain the blood system. For example, if the gut disease pernicious anaemia is preventing vitamin B_{12} from being absorbed, anaemia will develop no matter how much vitamin B_{12} is in the diet.

In other situations, the body may be using up more nutrients than it can obtain from a normal diet. For example, a woman with heavy periods may become iron deficient because of heavy bleeding. This can eventually cause iron deficiency because a normal diet will simply

not contain enough iron to make up the deficiency. The gut in this case will be working flat out to absorb as much iron as it can. Taking iron tablets for a few weeks should help to relieve the anaemia.

SMOKING, EXCESS ALCOHOL AND OTHER RISKY BEHAVIOURS

Apart from damaging the lining of the blood vessels, smoking increases the stickiness of platelets, which in turn increases the risk of strokes and heart attacks. Very excessive alcohol drinking can harm the blood and immune system, usually through damage to other organs, such as the liver. Unsafe sex (without a condom) or sharing a needle when using a hypodermic syringe allows the HIV virus to spread from one person to another.

PRESCRIBED DRUGS

Prescribed drugs frequently affect the blood and immune system. Most cytotoxic chemotherapy drugs used to treat cancer will rapidly decrease the body's ability to fight off infection. Other drugs can also affect the blood, usually in less predictable or dramatic ways. For example, aspirin and related drugs can cause a stomach ulcer. This may be so small that it does not

environmental pollution

infections

poor nutrition

smoking and excessive alcohol

genetics

Disorders affecting the blood and immune system
Some common and not so common diseases and disorders of the body's blood and lymph systems are listed below, with an indication of the number of new cases diagnosed each year in the UK.

LESS COMMON

HODGKINS DISEASE
3 PER 100,000 MEN
(1 IN 33,300); 1.8 PER 100,000
WOMEN (1 IN 55,550)

SCID (SEVERE COMBINED
IMMUNODEFICIENCY)
1 PER 100,000 BABIES

Milestones
IN MEDICINE

The very first blood bank was opened in 1932 in Leningrad. Five years later, the first blood bank outside the USSR was established in Chicago by Dr Bernard Fantus at Cook County Hospital. By setting up a hospital laboratory that could preserve and store donor blood, Fantus kick-started a movement that saw more than 1500 blood banks established in the USA by 1950. Britain's first blood bank was set up in Ipswich, Suffolk, in 1938, and a national Blood Transfusion Service was launched in 1946.

cause any pain, but the ulcer is constantly very slowly bleeding. This slow blood loss usually results in iron deficiency anaemia.

GENETIC AND HEREDITARY FACTORS

Scientists are beginning to understand a lot more about how genes are responsible for many blood and immune system diseases. Abnormal genes can be inherited or can be mutations. Many inherited genetic diseases are described as being autosomal recessive. This means that an abnormal gene has to be inherited from each parent for the disease to be apparent in their child. Because two copies of the abnormal gene are required, these diseases tend to be rare, unless parents are related to one another. Some types of severe combined immunodeficiency are inherited in this way.

Another type of inheritance is X chromosome linked (see page 155). If a woman inherits an X-linked disorder, she does not have its symptoms, but can be a carrier and so may pass the disorder on to some of her children. A man who inherits an X-linked disorder will have symptoms. Haemophilia is an example of an X-linked disorder.

Some diseases vary in severity depending on how many abnormal genes the patient has inherited. For example, having one abnormal gene for haemoglobin can cause mild sickle cell trait, but inheriting two abnormal genes causes the more severe sickle cell disease (see page 153).

In all of these examples the abnormal gene is present in every cell in the body and will be passed on to future generations. All these inherited disorders can be identified by genetic testing.

When mutations cause problems like leukaemia or lymphoma, they are only present in the cancerous cells. The mutations are not present in egg cells or sperm cells and so cannot be passed to future generations.

AGEING

The commonest cancers of the blood system – chronic leukaemias – occur mainly in elderly people. In general, the kind of genetic mutations that cause cancerous changes in white blood cells tend to accumulate over a person's lifetime.

ENVIRONMENTAL PROBLEMS

Problems from the environment rarely damage the blood and immune system. Very occasionally, chemicals such as lead or benzene can damage the blood system. In the past, before the amount of lead in petrol and paint was restricted, anaemia due to lead poisoning was relatively common in children brought up in urban environments.

As far as we know, most of the different types of radiation do not often cause damage to the blood and immune system. Powerful ionising radiation, usually from radioactive sources, can sometimes cause cancers. Fortunately, most people are never exposed to these types of radiation.

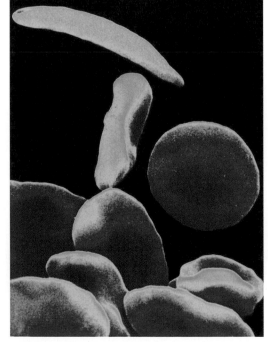

Sickle cell anaemia
Sickle cell disease – characterised by sickle-shaped red blood cells – is an example of a genetically inherited disease that affects the blood. Its main symptom is anaemia, which can be mild or severe.

Meet the blood and immune system experts

Since blood and lymph fluid circulate throughout the body, medical experts in diseases and disorders of the blood and immune system are not specialists in one organ only, but instead treat whichever part of the body is affected.

PATHOLOGIST

Pathologists are doctors who specialise in the study of disease. They are laboratory based and not generally involved in direct patient care. Certain types of pathologist specialise in the study of diseases and disorders of the blood and immune systems.

- **Histopathologists** (also known as morbid anatomists) carry out post mortems and check samples of tissue taken by biopsy from living patients for – say – cancer.
- **Microbiologists** look at other samples, such as urine or sputum, to check for and identify infection; they will also recommend appropriate treatments.
- **Chemical pathologists** (clinical biochemists) run tests on the body's biochemical system and are experts in diagnosing disorders such as thyroid disease.

Other pathologists – notably haematologists and immunologists – spend part of their time in laboratory investigations, but also deal with patients face to face.

IMMUNOLOGIST

Immunologists treat patients with diseases of the immune system, and run laboratory tests for diseases involving autoimmunity, immunodeficiency and also some cancers. Their work often overlaps with that carried out by allergists and rheumatologists.

ALLERGIST

Allergists are specialist doctors who diagnose allergies and advise on their treatment. They help to look after patients with problems ranging from rhinitis, eczema and asthma to life-threatening allergies such as anaphylaxis.

RHEUMATOLOGIST

Rheumatologists specialise in joint diseases. These doctors manage patients with common problems such as back ache and strain injuries, but also take on patients with more complex 'connective tissue diseases' like rheumatoid arthritis and systemic lupus erythematosus (SLE).

HAEMATOLOGIST

Haematologists are specially trained to interpret results of investigations into diseases of the blood. They have a particular expertise in looking at blood and bone marrow films. The majority of haematologists also look after patients, who may suffer from disorders and diseases of the blood ranging from common conditions like anaemia to complex, lifelong diseases such as haemophilia.

ONCOLOGIST AND RADIOTHERAPIST

Once a diagnosis has been made – probably with the assistance of a histopathologist – a cancer patient may be referred to a team of cancer specialists including an oncologist, a radiotherapist and a specialist surgeon, as appropriate. An oncologist knows how to treat cancer with drugs. Radiotherapists administer radiation treatment for cancer.

BLOOD TRANSFUSION SERVICE

Blood transfusion services play an essential role in recruiting donors, ensuring their blood is safe and overseeing blood donations. They make sure hospitals are well supplied with blood, that it is stored correctly and that the right blood goes into the correct patient. Some also extract blood products from whole blood.

TRANSPLANT SERVICE

Transplant services facilitate the removal of organs and tissues from donors (living or dead) and the identification of the most appropriate recipient.

FINDING OUT WHAT IS WRONG

One of the first things a medical student learns is how to take a thorough patient history and do an examination, following a set protocol. The history and examination can sometimes be enough to suggest a diagnosis of a blood or immunological disease. However, blood tests – and often other tests as well – are still generally required to confirm a diagnosis and to rule out other possible causes of symptoms.

Many of the tests described here can be carried out at the doctor's surgery. If problems are more complex, the doctor will refer the patient to a specialist, most probably a haematologist or an immunologist. Tests performed by these experts mostly take place in the hospital clinic and there is rarely a need for an overnight stay in hospital.

Medical history and examination

Before visiting the doctor it can be helpful to make notes of symptoms, to ensure that nothing is forgotten, and also to take along a list of any medications that are being taken, including dosages and timings.

TAKING A HISTORY
Obtaining an accurate patient history is an essential first step towards an accurate diagnosis.

Current complaint
The doctor will ask the patient for details of the problem. For example, if the problem is that the patient is feeling tired (possibly due to anaemia), the doctor will ask how long the patient has been feeling this way, what appears to worsen the fatigue and what alleviates it. The doctor will ask whether the patient has noticed any other symptoms – breathlessness or palpitations, for example – which may indicate anaemia.

Previous medical history
The doctor will try to establish whether the patient has experienced any illnesses in the recent or not-so-recent past that may have contributed to the current problem. For example, a doctor may ask a female patient whether she has had a succession of heavy periods – a common cause of anaemia.

Family history
The doctor will ask what illnesses other family members have experienced. This is important in diagnosing inherited disorders. If, for example, a parent and a brother or sister have both been anaemic, there is a good chance the patient has an inherited form of this condition.

Drug history
Establishing an accurate drug history is very important. This can give major clues to previous diagnoses; it also ensures that the doctor won't confuse drug side effects with symptoms of the patient's current complaint.

Aspirin and related drugs are often taken by people with aches and pains. If taken in excess, they can cause bleeding into the stomach and contribute to anaemia.

Diet

Most doctors are not trained to take a thorough dietary history, but they will be able to establish, for example, whether a patient's intake of iron is too low and may be causing anaemia. If a detailed dietary assessment is required, the doctor will refer the patient to a dietician.

Sex and relationships

Because sexually transmitted diseases are so common, the doctor may ask about the patient's sexual practices and partners. Some people find this awkward, but remember that the doctor does this dozens of times a week, won't feel embarrassed and shouldn't be shocked by anything.

The doctor also needs to ask about relationships in the patient's life. Relationships can contribute to stress and this may be relevant to the patient's physical and mental condition. In addition, the doctor may want to know whether there is a family member or friend who could take some responsibility for helping with treatment, should the need arise. For example, a confused patient may need someone at home to help plan and monitor the taking of their medication.

Occupational history

The doctor will often want to take details of employment, going back many years, because some occupations are associated with specific diseases. For example, chemical workers who have been exposed to benzene may be at higher risk of leukaemia.

Smoking, alcohol and recreational drug history

Because these substances can all be harmful to health, it is vital for the doctor to have honest details of whether and how much a patient

smokes, drinks or takes recreational drugs. The doctor is asking these questions for the patient's benefit and is not being judgmental. Even if a patient is doing something illegal, the conversation is confidential and the medical profession's standards demand that anything said will not go any further.

EXAMINATION

A physical examination can be a key element in the diagnosis of many diseases and disorders of the blood and immune system. The extent of the examination depends on the symptoms – if someone has a sore throat, for example, there is generally no need to examine the whole body. Some people find a full physical examination stressful. Any patient who feels particularly uncomfortable about being examined by a doctor of the opposite sex can ask to see a doctor of the same sex instead.

General appearance and skin

A lot of information can be gained from looking at a patient's general appearance. For example, the doctor might note that a patient has very pale skin and is lacking in energy, making anaemia a possibility. If there is

Looking for signs of anaemia
A doctor examines the inside of his patient's lower eyelid for signs of anaemia. A patient with anaemia may have a very pale inner eyelid. In addition, the patient's skin may be much paler than usual.

bruising, bone marrow failure may be a factor. If the patient's skin has a yellow tinge (jaundice), haemolytic anaemia may be suspected.

Cardiovascular system

The doctor will begin by taking the patient's pulse and blood pressure and then listening to the heart with a stethoscope. Although an infection or severe anaemia can cause a fast pulse, the cardiovascular system is not usually affected by blood or immune system disorders.

Lymph nodes

When examining a patient who is being checked for cancer or infection, it is usual to check for swollen lymph glands in the locality of the disease. So a doctor will check for swollen nodes in a patient's armpit if breast cancer is suspected. With some immune system and blood diseases, it is important to assess the lymph all over the body. The doctor does this by feeling for enlarged nodes

in the neck, armpits and groin. Some lymph nodes are situated deep in the chest and abdomen and these can only be assessed by CT or MRI scanning.

Chest

The most usual chest problem experienced by patients with problems with their blood or immune system is a chest infection. The doctor assesses how much air is entering the patient's chest by tapping lightly on the back or front, then listening to exactly how the breathing sounds. Although a doctor can often diagnose a chest infection by simply listening to the patient's chest and taking the patient's temperature, the doctor is likely to order a chest X-ray to confirm the presence of infection.

Abdomen

For the purposes of a patient's physical examination, the mouth is regarded as the first part of the abdomen. The mouth can show up many signs of disease – mucus membranes may look pale if the patient is anaemic, for example – and the fungal infection candidosis is often seen in the mouth in cases of immune deficiency.

Examining the lymphatic organs

a With some immune system and blood diseases, it is important to assess the lymph all over the body. The doctor does this by feeling for enlarged nodes in the neck, armpits and groin. Some lymph nodes are situated deep in the chest and abdomen and these can only be assessed by CT or MRI scanning.
b Haematologists are especially concerned about whether the spleen – the largest lymphoid organ of all – is enlarged, which can be a sign of some types of anaemia, lymphoma or leukaemia. The doctor palpates the patient's chest in order to feel the spleen – in the left upper part of the abdomen – whilst the patient breathes gently in and out.

Nervous system

The nervous system is not often affected by blood or immune system diseases, but the doctor should check that everything is working normally. This is done by asking the patient to move different parts of the body and face in turn, and then checking that the patient's ability to think and reason is as it should be.

Joints

Some blood disorders can include bleeding into the joints. In some immunological diseases – especially those affecting the connective tissue, such as systemic lupus erythematosus (SLE, see page 154) and rheumatoid arthritis – affected joints are swollen, warm and stiff. A doctor will examine each joint in turn to establish the full extent of the problem.

Blood tests

Blood tests are very important in the diagnosis of blood and immune system disorders. Most blood tests are done either at the doctor's surgery or in an outpatients clinic at a hospital. The most common blood test is the full blood count.

FULL BLOOD COUNT (FBC)

In a full blood count, an automated machine analyses the blood sample and counts and measures each of the different cell types.

The most frequently used result from a full blood count is the haemoglobin level. Anaemia is reflected by a low level of haemoglobin. The FBC can also give information on the cause of anaemia. For example, if the machine shows that red cells are small and pale, iron deficiency is the likely cause. If the red cells are larger than normal, then vitamin B_{12} or folate deficiency is likely, or alcoholic excess.

Reductions in the platelet count are much less common, but are seen in diseases like immune thrombocytopenia (ITP, see page 146), when bleeding can be a problem.

The white cell count is used for a variety of purposes. A raised neutrophil count is a useful clue in infections. A child with tummy pain who has a raised neutrophil count might have appendicitis, for example. If the child has a normal white cell count, the diagnosis is more likely to be a less serious problem like constipation.

Some results show a reduced neutrophil count, a condition named neutropenia. This can happen after chemotherapy and in some immunodeficiency diseases. It suggests that the patient is very vulnerable to infection and may need to take special precautions. In other

Taking a blood sample
The process of piercing a vein to remove a blood sample is called venepuncture. A strap around the upper arm compresses the arm to make the veins stand out. The blood is then drawn out of the arm by a syringe and into a vacutainer, which resembles a small test tube.

situations, the blood count may show changes in the number of lymphocytes in the blood. Increased lymphocyte numbers may be the result of infection or leukaemia; flow cytometry is required to distinguish between the two causes.

BLOOD FILM

Much less often, a raised white cell count can suggest problems like leukaemia. In such a case, a haematologist will examine the blood through a microscope. This is done by making a blood film, by spreading a very thin layer of blood onto a glass slide. The slide is processed so that each of the different cells is stained a different colour.

Using a blood film, haematologists can recognise leukaemic white blood cells from their unusual appearance, although occasionally flow cytometry is required to make the diagnosis.

What is measured in a full blood count?

A full blood count records the number, appearance and size of the different blood cells in the sample by counting:
- the red blood cells, together with the amount of oxygen-rich haemoglobin contained within them;
- the number of white blood cells in total;
- the number of the different kinds of white blood cells, such as neutrophils and lymphocytes;
- the platelets, which help the blood to clot so that bleeding is stopped.

ASK THE EXPERT

TESTING FOR IRON, FOLATE AND B$_{12}$

These tests investigate the cause of a patient's anaemia, but they are not always the end of the story. For example, for someone with low levels of iron it would be vital to check that there is no internal bleeding. If the folate or vitamin B$_{12}$ levels are low, then it becomes necessary to rule out disease of the stomach and small bowel, which could be impairing absorption of these vitamins.

BLOOD CLOTTING TESTS

These tests show whether the proteins that clot the blood are working correctly. For instance, if a sample from a boy suspected of having haemophilia (perhaps because of a family history of abnormal bleeding) was found to clot more slowly than normal, this would reinforce the suspected diagnosis. To confirm the diagnosis, it is then necessary to show that the boy's Factor VIII levels are low.

Checking up on anticoagulants

Much more frequently, clotting tests are used to check how well anticoagulants are working. Anticoagulants are drugs used to delay blood clotting when there has been a thrombosis (a venous thrombosis or pulmonary embolus, for example). If there has already been a blood clot, these drugs will prevent the clot from getting any bigger.

Anticoagulants can be given by injection (heparin) or by mouth (warfarin). It is very important to make sure the drugs are working correctly. If the blood is not anticoagulated enough, there is a risk of more clotting. If the blood is anticoagulated too much, there will be a risk of bleeding. Patients respond differently to the same dose of anticoagulants and other factors can destabilise expected results. For example, a course of antibiotics can either increase or decrease clotting ability.

For these reasons, patients on anticoagulants need regular clotting tests, usually every month or so. If the clotting test results have changed, a doctor may recommend changing the dose of anticoagulant.

THYROID FUNCTION TESTS

Thyroid function tests are blood tests which measure the amount of thyroxine and are used to diagnose this group of diseases. Thyroid function tests are also used to monitor patients with thyroid disease once they are receiving treatment. The thyroid gland secretes a hormone called thyroxine, which has widespread effects on the metabolism of the whole body. The thyroid can secrete

Clotting tests and meningococcal septicaemia
Sometimes people with serious injuries or infections can begin to have problems with blood clotting. An example is meningococcal septicaemia. This causes small bruises in the skin because the bacteria causing the infection trigger off abnormal clotting. This depletes the amount of clotting proteins available, and bleeding elsewhere can become a problem. In this case, clotting test results will be abnormal.

too much thyroxine (resulting in hyperthyroidism, for example in Graves' disease) or too little thyroxine, causing hypothyroidism, as in Hashimoto's disease.

COOMBS' TEST

In Coombs' test, a sample of blood taken from a patient is examined to find out whether the patient's red cells are being attacked by antibodies. This happens (hopefully not often) if blood of an incorrect group is transfused into a patient. Sometimes it can happen because the immune system attacks the body's own cells – a condition known as autoimmune haemolytic anaemia (see page 143). Coombs' test could be used in either of these situations.

HAEMOGLOBIN ELECTROPHORESIS

Some people inherit abnormal genes for haemoglobin, the red pigment in the red blood cells that carries oxygen from lungs to the tissues. If the haemoglobin is abnormal the red cells can become damaged and even destroyed, causing types of anaemia. The two common forms are sickle cell disease and thalassaemia. These are diagnosed by haemoglobin electrophoresis. Electrophoresis is a process for distinguishing between slightly different proteins; in this case it distinguishes between normal and abnormal haemoglobin.

FLOW CYTOMETRY

Flow cytometers fire lasers at each cell in a blood sample and collect data on how the laser beam is bounced back to a light detector. A flow cytometer can look at several thousand white cells in a few seconds and distinguish each of them on the basis of subtle differences in size, how granular they are, and different molecules on the surface of the cells. This type of counting could not possibly be done by human beings looking down microscopes, and many advances in immunology and haematology have resulted from this technology. Flow cytometers can count even tiny numbers of abnormal cells mixed in with the normal cells.

Advantages of flow cytometry over blood film

In many cases it is possible for haematologists or immunologists to find out what they are looking for by examining the different populations of white cells on a blood film. However, some of the different populations look the same under the microscope. For instance, the different populations of lymphocytes – helper T cells, B cells and cytotoxic cells – may all appear to be identical. In some situations it is necessary to distinguish between and count these different cells.

For example, an increase in the number of lymphocytes shown up by a blood count may be the result of infection or may reflect leukaemia. If there is an infection, it is usual for a mixed population of B cells and helper T cells to cause the increase in the number of lymphocytes, and each cell will be different from all the others. In leukaemia, the lymphocytes will all be the daughter cells of one single cancerous cell. This means that all the lymphocytes will, for example, be B cells, and each one will have identical molecules on its surface. Flow cytometry is the only way of

Flow cytometry

A technician uses a flow cytometer to analyse a blood sample. The blood cells have been tagged with a fluorescent antibody that binds to certain types of cells. The cells are then passed in single file through a beam of light, which causes tagged cells to fluoresce so they can be counted on a detector.

making the leukaemia diagnosis in this situation. After a patient has had treatment for leukaemia, flow cytometry is used to check whether the cancerous cells have been completely cleared. Even if only 1 in 10,000 lymphocytes in the blood was cancerous, it would be possible for this one cell to reproduce itself, causing a return of the leukaemia once treatment has stopped.

Monitoring HIV infections

HIV infection damages the immune system by destroying the helper T cells. This damage happens gradually over several years. Patients with HIV do not need treatment unless there are high levels of HIV in the blood – detected by polymerase chain reaction (PCR), see page 109 – or the helper T cell count has become low. Flow cytometry is the only way of accurately counting the number of helper cells in the blood. Helper T cells are distinguished from other cells by having a high level of a molecule called CD4 on their surface. Flow cytometers count the number of cells with CD4 on the surface, so the helper T cell count is sometimes referred to as the CD4 count.

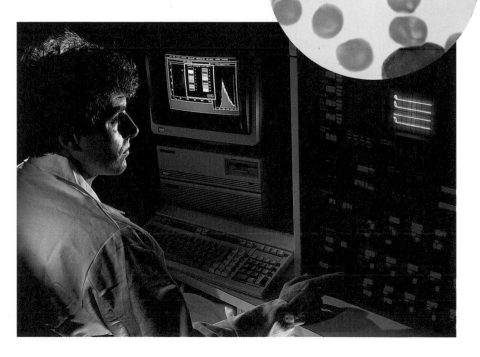

This blood film *shows three myeloblast cells, which indicate acute myeloblastic leukaemia.*

Bone marrow tests

There are two important bone marrow tests: the bone marrow aspirate, in which liquid bone marrow is sucked out with a needle, and the bone marrow trephine (also called a biopsy), in which a core of solid bone is taken.

Bone marrow tests are often much more useful than blood films for explaining the reason behind a blood problem. This is because bone marrow is the place where the red blood cells, platelets and most white blood cells are manufactured, and so by examining the bone marrow it is possible to inspect the blood manufacturing process.

WHAT ARE THEY USED FOR?

In a patient with a low platelet count, for example, the doctor can tell from a marrow sample whether the blood manufacturing process is working. If platelets are not being produced, this is one cause of a low platelet count (bone marrow failure). If platelets are being produced, they must be being destroyed elsewhere in the body (as in the spleen in immune thrombocytopenia, see page 146).

The most serious problems with manufacturing white cells are leukaemia and lymphoma, and bone marrow tests are particularly useful in diagnosing these diseases.

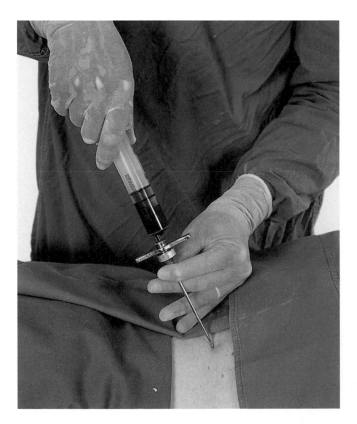

HOW ARE THEY DONE?

Both procedures can be done in an outpatients clinic in about half an hour: adults do not have to be admitted to hospital. Small children usually have bone marrow tests done under a general anaesthetic.

Both tests begin by cleaning the skin with a disinfectant such as iodine. Next, the doctor will inject local anaesthetic into the skin. This takes a few seconds to work. Because the procedures aim to take samples from the middle of the bones, the next step is to anaesthetise the bone itself. Bone is very sensitive to pain and injecting local anaesthetic into the bone is likely to be painful for the first few seconds.

Bone marrow aspirate

The aspirate can be taken from the iliac crest (the back of the pelvic bones) or the sternum (the breastbone). A wide bore needle is inserted into the middle of the bone and the semi-liquid marrow is sucked out into a syringe. Very often, a bone marrow aspirate is all that is needed.

Bone marrow trephine

The trephine is usually taken from the iliac crest. Undergoing the bone marrow trephine procedure is rather more uncomfortable than the aspirate because it takes a core of bone marrow and solid bone. This is most useful when doctors want to look at how cells are arranged in the bone marrow, which is not possible with a liquid sample. Cancer and some haematological problems can only be diagnosed by doing a trephine.

After the procedure

Once the procedure is complete, a patient is requested to lie down for an hour or so before being allowed home. When the local anaesthetic wears off, the patient may feel a dull ache at the site from where the sample was taken.

Taking a sample of bone marrow aspirate
Semi-liquid bone marrow – the aspirate – is sucked out into a syringe from a puncture made into the back of the patient's pelvis. The aspiration is being done to test the functioning of the patient's marrow.

Breakthroughs in genetic testing

The mapping of the human genome – the 23 pairs of chromosomes that make up each cell in the human body – has triggered major advances in medical research. Among disorders of the blood and immune system, genetic testing has improved diagnosis of leukaemia and HIV infection.

CYTOGENETIC ANALYSIS

There are 22 pairs of identical chromosomes and one pair of sex chromosomes in every normal cell. Cytogenetic testing is a way of checking that chromosomes are not damaged. It is especially important in two situations:

- Testing for chronic myeloid leukaemia In some people, chromosomes are damaged and genes become mixed up. This can lead to leukaemia. For example, a damaged chromosome (the 'Philadelphia chromosome') occurs often in chronic myeloid leukaemia. Cytogenetic testing for the Philadelphia chromosome is both a diagnostic test and a way of measuring response to treatment.

- Prenatal testing for Down's syndrome before birth In some genetic diseases chromosomes are damaged in very specific ways. In Down's syndrome there are three copies of chromosome number 21. Because only a few cells are needed to carry out cytogenetic testing, tiny samples of the fluid surrounding a fetus can be tested for cells with an extra chromosome 21 to check for Down's syndrome before birth.

Polymerase chain reaction in action
By this technique the DNA of a single cell, treated with polymerase enzymes, is induced to replicate many times. This enables DNA to be amplified in sufficient quantities to facilitate genetic analysis. Many recent advances in cancer diagnosis, HIV treatment, gene therapy and the human genome project would not have been possible without the invention of PCR.

POLYMERASE CHAIN REACTION (PCR)

Using the PCR method of replicating sequences of DNA in a test tube, scientists are now able to read the sequence of DNA for any given gene more rapidly than ever before and this has been put to a number of uses.

- PCR can detect DNA mutations known to cause cancer or leukaemia. This is a useful diagnostic test for some cancers.

- PCR technologies can detect one leukaemia cell or cancer cell among a million normal cells. This means that it can detect a recurrence of the disease after treatment much earlier than with other checks.

- By measuring the precise amount of HIV (human immunodeficiency virus) in infected patients' blood, PCR helps specialists to decide the best time to start anti-HIV treatments. These 'viral load' tests are used alongside helper T cell (CD4) counts.

1 A selected segment of a DNA molecule is extracted from a blood sample.

2 The strands are separated by raising the temperature to about 95°C.

3 Synthetic DNA fragments are then added, with the temperature at 50°C. These bind to the two DNA strands.

4 The enzyme DNA polymerase is added, and with the temperature at about 70°C, an exact copy of the original DNA segment is created.

5 By repeatedly raising and lowering the temperature of the DNA strands, a great many copies are produced rapidly.

Antibody and allergy testing

An antigen is a substance – usually a protein – that the body regards as dangerous. To counteract the danger, the body produces a special kind of blood protein called an antibody that circulates in the plasma seeking to attack the antigen and render it harmless.

ELISA TESTING

An enzyme-linked immunosorbent assay (ELISA) test measures whether antibodies will bind onto a specific antigen. These tests are most often used to diagnose infection. During an infection, the immune system normally produces antibodies against the responsible virus or bacteria. It is usually much easier to diagnose infection by looking for antibodies than by looking for the virus or bacteria. Blood transfusion services use ELISA to check donated blood for antibodies against viral infections such as HIV and hepatitis B and C.

AUTOANTIBODY TESTS

Autoantibody tests are used to help diagnose autoimmune diseases. The tests work by seeing whether the patient's blood contains antibodies that bind onto normal healthy body tissues. For example, in pernicious anaemia

ELISA antibody test

Multi-pipettes are suspended over a multi-well sample tray in an ELISA test. To measure the amount of a target substance in the blood, an antibody that binds with the target substance is mixed with the blood sample.

autoantibodies are produced which bind to the stomach-lining cells that normally help the body to absorb vitamin B_{12}.

POLYMORPHISMS AND FORENSIC TESTING

Each individual has a group of human leucocyte antigens (HLA), DNA and proteins that is almost unique. Some people may have relatively common HLA genes, others may share their HLA genes with just one in every few thousand other people. These genetic differences between people are called polymorphisms.

Establishing paternity

Testing to identify genetic polymorphisms has been used in paternity cases, although, strictly speaking, genetic finger printing can rule out a potential father, but cannot completely confirm one. If a child shares polymorphisms with the suspected father he could have inherited them from him. If the man and child share no polymorphisms, then he couldn't possible be the father.

Forensic testing

DNA is very stable – even material from the ancient Egyptian tombs of the Pharaohs can be used to identify family trees. This characteristic makes genetic finger prints useful in criminal investigations. Tiny traces of DNA – for example, on a cigarette tip being used as a piece of evidence – can rule suspects out or in.

IMMUNOGLOBULIN AND PLASMA ELECTROPHORESIS

Immunoglobulins are structurally related proteins that act as antibodies. They are produced by the immune system and normally bind onto bacteria or viruses and destroy them. In autoimmune diseases, antibodies are produced that bind onto normal components of the body and cause disease rather than helping to protect the body against it.

Very high levels of immunoglobulins are also produced in some tumours, such as those associated with myeloma and lymphoma. Compared with normal antibodies produced in response to an infection, the immunoglobulins produced by tumour cells all have identical structures because they originate from one original cancerous cell. These identical cells and immunoglobulin are sometimes described as being monoclonal. In myeloma (see page 150) monoclonal immunoglobulins are found in the blood and in the urine.

How electrophoresis helps

Electrophoresis is a technique whereby electrically charged particles in solution (sometimes a serum or plasma) are separated into bands by having an electric current passed through them. Electrophoresis will show whether immunoglobulins are monoclonal. It can also show if levels of immunoglobulin are very low, which would indicate antibody deficiencies. People with low levels of immunoglobulin are very prone to recurrent chest and sinus infection. Immunoglobulin treatment can prevent infections getting any worse.

ALLERGY TESTING

Allergy testing aims to identify the substances to which a patient is allergic. The particular substances to which an individual is allergic – for example, peanuts, pollen or house dust mites – are referred to as allergens. Most allergies result in irritating symptoms, but some can be debilitating and in its most serious form – known as anaphylaxis – an allergic reaction can be life-threatening.

Safeguards in place before testing

Allergy tests should be carried out by either a medically trained allergist or a doctor with expertise in chest medicine, dermatology or paediatrics. The tests can be dangerous – there is always a chance of discovering an extreme anaphylactic reaction. For this reason there must always be resuscitation equipment and experienced, well-trained staff to hand.

There are three well-established tests for allergies. It should be borne in mind that test results are not always 100 per cent accurate, especially in the case of skin and

Electrophoresis in action
A laboratory technician is separating particles within a gel so that they form distinct bands. This is done by applying an electric field to the particles. The particles may be proteins, such as immunoglobulins, or DNA fragments. Normal or fluorescent dyes may be used to visualise the particles, or they may be labelled with radioisotopes.

challenge testing; the results may not actually reflect the true clinical situation.

Skin prick test

This is done by pricking a tiny amount of allergen into the outer layer of the skin. Within a few minutes, a patient who is truly allergic to the allergen will experience an itchy swelling up to 10mm (½ inch) in diameter on the surface of the skin. The itchiness may last as long as a couple of hours. Very rarely, there can be a more serious reaction, especially if the patient has a history of anaphylaxis. Substances that are harmless for an individual cause no swelling at all. If the patient is on antihistamine tablets, the tests may not work.

Challenge test

This is usually done to test for the cause of a suspected food allergy. In the safe environment of the clinic, the patient eats a tiny amount of the suspected allergen, usually made up into a biscuit. The reactions to the food can then be noted.

Allergy blood tests

Sometimes called specific IgE tests or RAST (radioallergosorbent) tests, allergy blood tests aim to show how much of the allergy-causing antibody – the IgE – a patient has that will act against a specific allergen.

Allergy blood tests are much less reliable than skin prick testing. They are reserved for situations when skin prick testing is unsafe (where there is a history of anaphylaxis or eczema, or in very young children) or when the patient has been taking antihistamines.

CURRENT TREATMENTS

Medical aid is at hand for a wide range of conditions affecting the blood and immune system. More sophisticated drugs than ever before are now available for the control and treatment of diseases and disorders. Doctors use chemotherapy and radiotherapy to treat cancers of the blood and lymphatic systems; after cancer treatment, stem cell transplantation is available if needed to repair a patient's damaged bone marrow cells. A recent major breakthrough is stem cell gene therapy – used to treat severe combined immunodeficiency (SCID) in children.

Drugs for blood and the immune system

Drugs are not only used to treat the causes of diseases and disorders of the blood and immune system, but also the adverse side effects of other treatments.

AN OVERVIEW OF PRESCRIBED DRUG USE

Drugs help to treat diseases and disorders of the blood and immune system in many different ways.

- There are drugs that stop unwanted blood clotting, and also drugs that help to clot the blood.
- A primary weapon in the fight against cancers of the blood is the use of drugs in chemotherapy. These drugs kill as many cancerous blood cells as possible – but healthy cells are also destroyed, meaning almost inevitably that a patient's ability to fight off infection is seriously impaired. Antibiotics are often prescribed to help patients while their immune system recovers. Interferons are also prescribed to inhibit tumour cells.
- Drugs are used to suppress the automatic attempts of the body's immune system to reject a 'foreign' organ that has been transplanted into the body, and also after stem cell transplantation.
- Drugs also help fight immunosuppressive diseases, as with drugs prescribed to combat HIV infection.

Drugs used for treating HIV infection

The goal of drug therapy against HIV infection (see page 144) is to increase the length and quality of life by improving the immune function. This is achieved by reducing the amount of replicating virus to as low a level as possible, for as long as possible, in all sites where HIV-infected cells are present, thereby preventing infection of new cells and further damage to the immune system. There are currently three classes of anti-HIV drugs in use in the UK. They are often prescribed in combination with each other.

NRIs (NUCLEOSIDE TRANSCRIPTASE INHIBITORS) NRI zidovudine (AZT) was the first anti-HIV drug. NRIs are generally well tolerated but side effects can include nausea and fatigue.

PIs (PROTESE INHIBITORS) A dramatic decline in the clinical progression of HIV disease and HIV-related deaths followed the introduction of PIs in 1996. There are many tablets to take, and there may be adverse side effects; PIs can't be taken with some common prescription drugs, such as antihistamines and the oral contraceptive pill, or with some foods.

NNRTIs (NON-NUCLEOSIDE REVERSE TRANSCIOTASE INHIBITORS) Resistance to these drugs develops quickly, but they are a lot simpler to take than PIs; there may be adverse side effects such as drowsiness or rashes.

Drugs that prevent blood clotting

Drugs taken to prevent the blood from clotting are most often given to patients who are naturally at risk of forming blood clots inside blood vessels, or following surgery, or during kidney dialysis. These drugs can be taken by mouth or injection.

Blood clots usually form as a response to injury. When a clot forms for some other reason, there is a risk that it might become lodged in a blood vessel and even block the blood supply to the heart or brain. There are two sorts of drugs that doctors prescribe to stop abnormal blood clotting: anticoagulants and antiplatelet drugs.

Drugs given by injection take immediate effect; taken by mouth, they will work after a few days. The effect of anticoagulants and antiplatelet drugs can be enhanced or reduced by other drugs and illnesses, and so patients must keep their GP informed of any changes in their health or medication. People taking such drugs orally over the long-term need to carry a card that outlines their treatment.

ANTICOAGULANTS

These drugs reduce the effectiveness of the coagulation factors within the blood that promote blood clotting; which factors are affected varies from drug to drug. The two most commonly used drugs are heparin and warfarin.

• **Heparin** is given by injection and acts rapidly, but is only effective for a short time. It is used in hospitals during or after surgery to prevent clot formation, and during kidney dialysis to prevent clots forming in dialysis machines. Heparin can also stabilise existing clots so fragments don't break away and travel to other parts of the body. Lengthy operations – especially those involving the pelvis, hips or knees – can lead to deep vein thrombosis (DVT). Low doses of heparin reduce the incidence of DVT and fatal embolism in patients undergoing general surgery by 60–70 per cent.

Too much heparin can cause bleeding, which is why treatment has to be carefully supervised. Newer versions of heparin, called low-molecular-weight heparins (dalteparin, enoxaparin, tinzaparin) are longer-lasting and need less monitoring.

• **Warfarin** is the most widely used oral anticoagulant. It is generally taken long-term, as a preventative treatment for patients at risk of a stroke, heart attack or disturbed heart rhythms (atrial fibrillation), or who have an artificial heart valve. It interferes with vitamin-K-dependant synthesis of clotting factors. Its use is

Are drugs ever taken to encourage blood clotting – and thereby stop bleeding?

When bleeding is difficult to stop – as after surgery, sometimes – clotting can be encouraged by using an antifibrinolytic such as tranexamic acid. This drug can also be given to haemophiliacs before dental surgery and other minor operations. Severe bleeding in haemophiliacs may be treated by injecting into the blood a concentrated form of the Factor VIII that is missing from a haemophiliac's blood.

ASK THE EXPERT

monitored in regular blood tests at the start of treatment to measure its effect on clotting time. The dosage is adjusted during this phase. Bleeding is the main side effect of oral anticoagulants and doctors will have an emergency plan of what to do in the event of bleeding.

ANTIPLATELET DRUGS

Antiplatelet drugs prevent clots forming by binding to platelets in the blood and lessening their ability to stick together and form clots.

• **Aspirin** helps to thin the blood and is taken long term, in low doses, by many people at risk of blood clots in the blood circulatory system and/or of stroke, heart attack, angina or atherosclerosis.

• **Dipyridamole** can be taken in combination with aspirin to reduce the risk of a second stroke. This drug dilates the blood vessels as well as inhibiting platelets.

• **Clopidogrel** is taken to help prevent heart attacks and strokes. It can also be taken with aspirin, and the two together have been shown to be more effective than aspirin alone.

THROMBYLOTIC AGENTS

These are used to dissolve clots already in existence. The most common thrombolytics (also known as fibrinolytics) are streptokinase and alteplase.

Treating anaemia

The word anaemia comes from the Ancient Greek for 'lack of blood'. Medically, the term is used to indicate a shortage of haemoglobin – the oxygen-carrying proteins in red blood cells. Treatments for this common condition vary, depending on the cause.

FINDING THE CAUSE

Whether a patient is anaemic can be settled quickly and easily by means of a blood test. A low level of haemoglobin in the blood indicates anaemia. Effective treatment of anaemia, however, depends on establishing its precise cause. So before treatment can begin, further tests are necessary to find the exact mechanism responsible. For example, initial tests may show that the cause is iron deficiency, but then the doctor must determine why the body has run out of iron. Tests can include: bone marrow aspiration (see page 108); genetic testing; X-rays and other imaging scans to pick up problems to do with organs such as the stomach, intestines, liver or kidneys.

Once the cause of the anaemia has been diagnosed, treatment can be decided upon and commenced. Treatments range from simply having to take iron tablets once a day or vitamin B_{12} injections every month to complex operations, such as a splenectomy for autoimmune haemolytic anaemia (see page 143).

Eat to beat anaemia
Anaemia due to a diet deficient in iron or folate can be treated with an iron and folate-rich diet, or iron and folic acid supplements. These dietary changes may also help with anaemia due to regular loss of blood.

Anaemia due to iron deficiency

A low haemoglobin count due to lack of iron is the most common cause of anaemia. The two main reasons are loss of iron through slow, chronic bleeding (heavy periods are a common cause of anaemia) or (less commonly) an iron-deficient diet. Slow intermittent internal bleeding, as from a gastric or duodenal ulcer, can be stopped by surgery. Blood transfusions are rarely given just to treat anaemia.

Anaemia from vitamin B_{12} deficiency

Anaemia arising from vitamin B_{12} deficiency is rarely due to poor diet alone, unless the patient's diet is very restricted. The problem generally lies in the body's inability to absorb vitamin B_{12} and is controlled by regular injections of vitamin B_{12}.

Anaemia arising from bone marrow failure

Bone marrow can fail to make or sustain a sufficient number of red blood cells because of cancer; or as an aftereffect of cancer treatment, such as chemotherapy. In this case the treatment is generally stem cell transplants into the bone marrow (see page 120).

Anaemia from genetic disorders

There are genetic blood disorders which lead to abnormalities within haemoglobin molecules. The two most common are thalassaemia (see page 154) and anaemia from sickle cell disease (see page 153).

In the case of thalassaemia, the standard treatment is regular blood transfusions. Sickle cell anaemia is best tackled by means of antibiotics and folic acid taken on a regular basis. In a sickle cell crisis – a flare-up of the disease – a blood transfusion may be needed.

Haemolytic anaemia

Haemolytic anaemia occurs when red blood cells are broken down prematurely. There are different causes, and the treatment options vary according to the cause (see page 142).

Blood transfusions

A patient needs a blood transfusion when blood is being lost at such a rate that the body can't make up the loss on its own – common causes are accidental injury or surgery. Occasionally a transfusion is ordered to treat anaemia that won't respond to other medicines.

Before recommending a blood transfusion or treatment with blood products, doctors need to make a risk assessment. This means that the doctor must balance the possible benefits of a transfusion against the potential risks. For example, someone who is bleeding because he or she has just been knocked over by a bus may well need a life-saving blood transfusion. The tiny risk of infection is overwhelmed by the serious effects of the haemorrhage.

WHAT CAN GO WRONG

• **Infection** A patient may become infected with a blood-borne virus during the blood transfusion process. This now happens only rarely, thanks to the tests done on blood donors before they give blood (see page 55).

• **Blood mismatch** A patient may be given blood of the wrong group. If this happens, antibodies in the recipient's blood will attack the donated cells and destroy them. To prevent this, not only is the patient's blood group carefully established, but, as a second check, a sample of the patient's antibodies in serum is mixed with blood cells belonging to the donor; this is called a cross-match. Units of blood identified by this test as safe for the recipient are then labelled and held in a fridge until needed. Then, just before the unit of blood is transfused, two nurses read off the patient's name, date of birth and hospital number from the label and confirm that the blood is going to the right person.

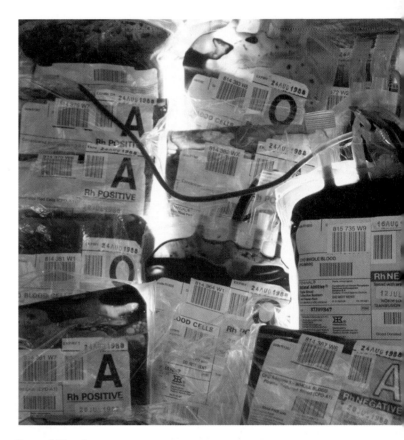

Bags of blood
Donated blood awaits collection at a blood transfusion centre. Blood is classified as A, B, AB or O, and as Rhesus positive or negative. A, B and O are different molecules that the immune system of the recipient of a blood transfusion may recognise as foreign.

• **Feverish reactions** A patient may develop a fever during a transfusion because the immune system recognises proteins in the donated blood. The fever is usually mild.

BLOOD PRODUCTS FOR TRANSFUSION

Donated blood is either left whole or separated out into red blood cells, platelets and plasma. The blood is spun at high speed to separate it into red blood cells and plasma. Then, if necessary, the plasma is spun (centrifuged) to draw out the platelets. Most transfusions that take place use whole blood or red blood cells suspended in a special nutrient solution.

AT THE LEADING EDGE

One blood type for all

Scientists at the New York Blood Center are trying to create a 'universal' donor blood for transfusion to do away with the problem of patients needing compatible blood. So far, they have managed to convert type B blood into type O, and this is now being used in clinical trials. They are also well on the way to being able to convert type A blood to type O (a more complicated procedure), and remove the rhesus factor.

Platelet transfusions

Platelets are tiny packets of cytoplasm that play a crucial role in the blood-clotting process (see page 24). They are given to people with dangerously low platelet counts, such as those suffering from the platelet disorder immune thrombocytopenic purpura (ITP) or bone marrow failure (see page 138). Usually, donations from six different people are required to give a patient enough platelets.

Plasma transfusions

Plasma is a solution of proteins. Whole plasma is given to:
• patients with conditions such as serious burns or infections, to try to restore their damaged blood-clotting mechanism;
• patients who have problems with low blood pressure.
Plasma is also broken down – known as fractionated – to produce different proteins, including:
• Factor VIII, for haemophilia;
• albumen, sometimes given to people in shock;
• anti D antibody, for haemolytic disease of the newborn;
• immunoglobulin, for antibody deficient patients.
Some of these proteins are present in plasma only in small amounts. Plasma from hundreds, even thousands, of donors is mixed in order to yield enough proteins and to make the fractionation process economical. A problem with mixing or 'pooling' plasma from many donors is the increased risk of the finished product carrying blood-borne infection. The risk of infection with hepatitis or HIV from plasma is now very low, because of donor screening.

From donor to freezer
After blood has been donated at a transfusion centre, it is sent to a blood bank where it is processed before storage. A technician is shown here setting up automated extraction of plasma from donated blood. After separation, the plasma is frozen until needed.

SCREENING BLOOD DONORS

Donors are asked questions about the risk of infection before they are allowed to give blood. Each blood donation is then tested for HIV, hepatitis and other infections. Plasma and fractionated products undergo further treatments to ensure they are safe. For example, they may be heat treated so that doctors are as certain as they can be that any viruses that have escaped the testing process have been removed.

At the moment, blood donors can't be tested for variant Creutzfeld Jacob disease (vCJD), which could theoretically spread through plasma products. To reduce this risk, blood from UK donors is not fractionated. All the fractionation taking place in the UK is done using plasma imported from overseas. The US Government has taken things a step further. They have told their transfusion services that people who have visited the UK for long periods should not be allowed to donate blood at all.

Drug treatments for cancers of the blood

When fighting cancers of the blood and the immune system, the first line of attack is generally the use of drugs to kill as many cancer cells as possible. Antibiotics also come into play, to combat the patient's susceptibility to infection after chemotherapy.

CHEMOTHERAPY

Chemotherapy is a term associated with administration of drugs as a method of cancer treatment. The drugs used to kill cancer cells are also called cytotoxics.

Chemotherapy is used to treat various cancers affecting the blood and immune systems. All cells, whether normal or cancerous, go through phases of growth and development during their life cycle, and chemotherapy drugs interfere with the cellular activities during one or more of these phases. The drugs circulate in the blood to achieve a total body (systemic) effect.

The choice of chemotherapy for each patient depends on the type and location of the cancer, its stage of development, and the general health of the patient. In most cases the dose is calculated from the height and weight of the patient, and given by mouth, injection or through a special intravenous line. It is standard practice to administer a combination of drugs, each exerting different effects and acting on specific stages of the cell cycle. At the same time, combining drugs reduces the chance of drug resistance developing.

Malignant cells have a less effective repair capacity than normal cells, so chemotherapy is given intermittently rather than at a constant low dose; this allows the healthy cells a breathing space in which to recover. The length and frequency of chemotherapy depends on the type of cancer, the drugs being used and how the patient responds to them, and drugs can be given daily, weekly, or monthly. A cycle is established, with the next treatment occurring once the normal stem cells have had enough time to recover from the last. Sometimes treatment is given in an on-and-off cycle that includes rest periods so the body has a chance to build healthy new cells and regain strength. Drugs known as growth factors are now available to accelerate the body's recovery of blood cell production.

Possible side effects

One of the main problems with chemotherapy is that normal cells are killed as well as cancer cells. Side effects depend on which normal cells are affected.

Venous access through a Hickman catheter
A patient receiving chemotherapy over a period of months needs a long-term venous access device. A Hickman catheter made of silicone rubber allows chemotherapy to be given into a large central vein (the vena cava) or directly into the right atrium of the heart.

- Bone marrow damage can lead to infections and bleeding – overcome by antibiotics and platelets.
- Damage to the gastrointestinal tract can cause a sore mouth, nausea and diarrhoea.
- Damage to hair follicles can cause temporary hair loss.
- Damage to the reproductive organs can cause infertility, but both eggs and sperm can be frozen.

TARGETED TREATMENT WITH MONOCLONAL ANTIBODIES

Monoclonal antibodies are a new class of drugs specially designed to recognise malignant cells, bind to them and destroy them. An anti-CD20 antibody (rituximab) is active against lymphoma cells, anti-CD33 antibody against acute myeloid leukaemia cells, and anti-CD52 against chronic lymphocytic leukaemia cells. Targeting the attack on cancerous cells cuts down on many of the adverse effects of broad-based chemotherapy treatments, which damage healthy cells in addition to cancerous ones. Unfortunately there may still be side effects such as rash, fever and shivering. And anti-CD20 and anti-CD52 antibodies can impair the immune system, increasing the risk of viral infections.

Drugs for treating cancers associated with blood and the immune system

Some of the drugs currently being used to treat haematological cancers are listed below. The drugs mostly work by inhibiting DNA synthesis or damaging DNA, thereby preventing cells from growing and dividing. Side effects vary, with some patients experiencing far fewer side effects than others. In addition to the side effects listed, almost all the drugs reduce blood-cell production by bone marrow, resulting in a low blood count, often leading to infection, anaemia and bleeding; other common side effects are nausea and hair loss.

Drug name	Drug type	Used to treat	Possible adverse effects
methotrexate (MTX)	antimetabolite	lymphomas; acute lymphoblastic leukaemia; meningeal leukaemia	mucositis (inflammation of gastrointestinal tract); diarrhoea; liver damage; lung problems
cytosine arabinoside (Ara-C)	antimetabolite	acute myeloid leukaemia	poor appetite; sore mouth; slurred speech, staggered gait; conjunctivitis; liver damage; gut toxicity
6-mercaptopurine, 6-thioguannine	purine analogue antimetabolite	6-MP: acute lymphoblastic leukaemia 6-TG: chronic myeloid leukaemia	loss of appetite; sore mouth; liver damage
vincristine (Oncovin), vinblastine	vinca alkaloids	acute leukaemias; lymphomas	tingling and numbness of fingers and toes; muscular weakness
bleomycin	cytotoxic antibiotic	Hodgkin's disease; lymphomas	lung fibrosis; skin toxicity (redness, pigmentation, ulceration); fever and malaise
cyclophosphamide	alkylating agent	various haematological malignancies	bladder damage
doxorubicin, daunorubicin	anthracyclines	various haematological malignancies	mucositis; damage to heart if taken in excess
L-asparaginase	enzyme	lymphoid malignancies	problems with blood clotting more or less easily than before
dexamethasone, prednisolone	steroids	lymphoid malignancies	fluid retention; high blood pressure; diabetes; increased appetite; infection; osteoporosis
all-trans retinoic acid (ATRA)	derived from vitamin A	acute promyelocytic leukaemia	dry skin; abnormal liver function; fluid in lungs

ANTIBIOTICS AFTER CHEMOTHERAPY

A patient's white blood cell count can be affected by chemotherapy, leaving the patient vulnerable to infection during treatment. A very low white cell count is known as neutropenia (see page 146). The blood count is at its lowest 10 to 14 days following chemotherapy treatment, but the acute immunosuppressive effects of most drugs used in chemotherapy do not extend for prolonged periods beyond the time of active drug administration.

One of the main symptoms of infection is a high temperature; if this occurs, a patient should contact the doctor immediately, because antibiotics will be needed. Aggressive antibiotic therapy using antibiotics such as gentamicin, ceftazidime and vancomycin has greatly aided the treatment of infectious complications.

Some patients take an antibiotic called co-trimoxazole during treatment and for a while afterwards, to prevent a common lung infection, called pneumocystis, to which immunosuppressed patients are susceptible.

INTERFERON

Interferons are substances (produced by white blood cells and artificially in the laboratory) prescribed to patients to inhibit tumour cells from growing inside the body. Interferon alpha is able to slow tumour growth directly, as well as help to activate the immune system. It is used for the treatment of cancers including multiple myeloma, chronic myelogenous leukaemia and hairy cell leukaemia. Some patients respond better than others. A common side effect is a flu-like reaction with fever, fatigue and chills.

Lymph node removal

Lymph nodes are removed either to see whether cancerous cells are present – cells that have probably spread from a primary cancer site elsewhere – or when it is known that the nodes are cancerous and surgery is thought to be the best way to treat the malignancy.

Lymph nodes are small bean-like swellings that occur at intervals throughout the lymphatic system (see page 30). They are found in different parts of the body; in particular, there are groups of nodes in the neck and behind the ear, around the armpit, in the area of the groin, and in various locations within the abdomen.

LYMPH NODE BIOPSY

Because a lymph node biopsy involves an operation, it is usually only performed when other, simpler, tests have not been helpful. For example, swollen lymph nodes (lymphadenopathy, see page 135) can be caused by infections and in these cases blood tests for glandular fever or HIV may be sufficient for a diagnosis.

Fine needle aspiration

Some easily felt lymph nodes, just under the skin, can be biopsied using a fine needle: this is often called fine needle aspiration. A local anaesthetic makes this a painless process, and a hospital stay is not necessary. However, only small samples can be obtained by fine needle aspiration.

SURGICAL LYMPH NODE REMOVAL

For a biopsy involving deeper lymph nodes, or when a large sample is required, or when a number of lymph nodes are removed as a cancer treatment, patients are given a general anaesthetic and the lymph nodes are taken out by a surgeon. This requires a stay in hospital for a couple of days.

After the operation

Often, the only adverse effect is soreness that wears off in a few weeks. Sometimes, however, the removal of lymph nodes can cause a gradual swelling of the limb or area

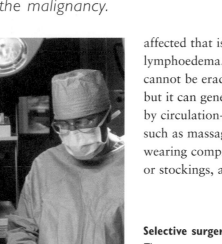

affected that is known as lymphoedema. Unfortunately, this cannot be eradicated completely, but it can generally be controlled by circulation-boosting activities such as massage, exercise and wearing compression sleeves or stockings, as appropriate.

Selective surgery
The surgeon removes only those lymph nodes in the region of the patient's breast that have been identified as cancerous by sentinel lymph node mapping.

AT THE LEADING EDGE

Sentinel lymph node mapping

The traditional way of testing for and arresting the spread of breast cancer is to remove 15 or more lymph nodes from the area surrounding the breast; only when they are examined in a laboratory does it become known which ones (if any) contained cancer cells. Inevitably damage to the nerves, muscle and other tissues surrounding the nodes means the patient faces a painful recovery, with stiffness, swelling and loss of movement in the affected arm that may be permanent. Now there is a new procedure called sentinel node mapping that is much less invasive. A few hours before the operation to remove lymph nodes, a radiologist injects a solution of radioactive tracer material and blue dye into the breast, around the site of the cancer. This solution will collect in any 'sentinel' lymph nodes in the area that contain cancerous cells. The surgeon then knows exactly which lymph nodes are cancerous and will take care to remove only these in the operation that follows.

Stem cell transplantation

Doctors can now take immature 'stem' cells, capable of developing into several different types of mature cell, and use them to boost the bone marrow of a patient whose marrow is starting to fail. Bone marrow transplant is a type of stem cell transplant.

WHAT ARE STEM CELLS?

Stem cells are very immature cells that have the capability to develop into a wide range of mature cells. Stem cells are present in large numbers in the blood of newborn babies. In adults they are harder to find, but are present in small quantities in the blood and especially in bone marrow. Stem cells from adult bone marrow have been shown to be capable of growing into mature brain cells. It is possible that in the future such cells could be used, for example, to treat patients who have severe spinal cord injuries. At the moment, the main medical use of stem cells is to replace stem cells in the recipient's bone marrow that have been damaged by chemotherapy.

TAKING STEM CELLS FROM BONE MARROW

Stem cells are removed relatively easily from the bone marrow. The donor is given a general anaesthetic and several bone aspirates are taken from the pelvic bones. About half a litre (one pint) of bone marrow is removed – this may yield several million stem cells.

It is also possible to remove stem cells from a donor's blood. First, the donor is given a course of injections to increase the number of stem cells in the circulation. Then some blood is taken and the stem cells are extracted from it. This process is less traumatic for the donor, but may yield fewer cells than bone marrow aspiration.

Conditioning the recipient's marrow

Prior to stem cell transplant, room must be made in the recipient's bone marrow. The recipient's marrow has to be destroyed by cytotoxic chemotherapy drugs, in order to allow the donor stem cells to produce a new marrow. This process is referred to as conditioning. In cases of cancer, lymphoma and leukaemia, these conditioning drugs will also help to eradicate cancer cells.

RECEIVING THE DONOR STEM CELLS

The donor's stem cells are infused intravenously into the recipient through a Hickman catheter inserted into a vein. It takes about a month for the new stem cells to grow and restore the blood counts to normal. During this period the recipient is kept in isolation within the hospital because of the increased likelihood of infection and bleeding associated with a low blood cell count. Sometimes the stem cells fail to multiply – this is known as graft failure.

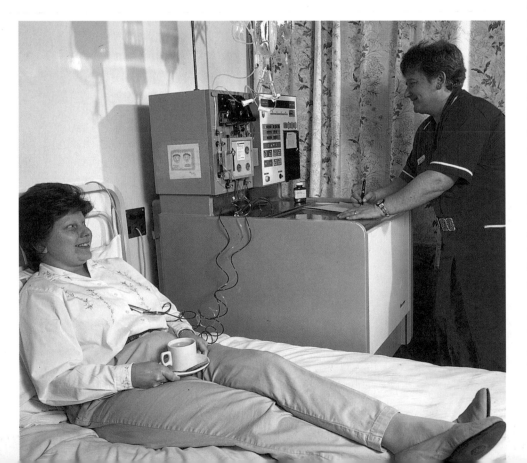

Peripheral blood stem cell (PBSC) donation
First the prospective PBSC donor is given an injection of natural growth factors to stimulate her bone marrow to produce PBSC extra to her own requirements. Then, as shown here, the donor's blood is run through a separating machine that removes the PBSCs, which will be given to a patient in need of PBSC transplantation.

WHEN STEM CELL TRANSPLANT IS NEEDED

- In babies with severe genetic problems affecting the cells of the bone marrow, such as babies with severe combined immunodeficiency (SCID) or thalassaemia.
- In cancers of the blood cells (leukaemia, lymphoma and myeloma) a stem cell transplant replaces bone marrow damaged by chemotherapy undertaken to reduce the number of cancerous cells made in the marrow. In some cases, initial chemotherapy reduces the number of malignant cells to almost zero. When some cancer cells remain, it may be possible to give stronger chemotherapy that will hopefully eradicate the cancer cells. But stronger chemotherapy almost always damages normal bone marrow cells and then stem cell transplant is required to replace the damaged marrow.
- In cases of bone marrow failure stem cell transplant may be used if other measures are not working. For example, when a patient has developed bone marrow failure (see page 139) after taking a particular drug, the drug is stopped and the patient is observed to see if the marrow will recover without extra help. If this does not happen, stem cell transplantation may be carried out.
- In some cases of severe autoimmune disease the patient's immune system continues to attack normal tissues even after strong immunosuppressive drugs have been given. To prescribe even more potent immunosuppressive drugs may control the autoimmune disease, but will also destroy the immune system and healthy bone marrow, making stem cell transplantation necessary.

AT THE LEADING EDGE

Stem cells from 'cord blood'

Recently, cord blood has been used as a source of stem cells. Cord blood is the blood left in the umbilical cord after it has been cut off a newborn baby. Normally it is thrown away. There is only about a quarter of a pint of blood in the umbilical cord and not many stem cells are present. However, the cells seem to be particularly good at regenerating a recipient's bone marrow and there may be a reduced risk of graft versus host disease, one of the most serious complications of stem cell transplant (see page 122). Cord blood can be frozen for several months.

In the future cord blood may be stored in special banks so that the stem cells can subsequently be used for anyone that needs them. Shown here is a test sample being taken from a bag of cord blood before a transfusion.

" DONATING BONE MARROW

When I registered as a potential bone marrow donor, the bone marrow registry took a blood sample to identify my HLA type and the information was entered on the registry computer.

Three years later the registry contacted me: they had a potential recipient for my bone marrow. I went to see them for more blood tests and a full medical, and, these having proved

OK, a date was set for the donation. I checked into the hospital the night before the operation. The procedure itself took about an hour and was performed under a general anaesthetic.

The surgeon had explained how he would use a hollow needle and syringe to extract about half a litre of marrow from my pelvic bones. When I came round I felt very tired, and also very

sore around my lower back. I spent the following night in hospital, recovering. The doctor told me it would take 4–6 weeks for my bone marrow to replenish itself. It was a few weeks before the soreness disappeared entirely, too.

Nevertheless, I feel happy that I was able to give the person who received my bone marrow a chance of recovery from their illness.

"

AUTOLOGOUS STEM CELL TRANSPLANT

The simplest form of stem cell transplant involves using the patient's own marrow. It is particularly appropriate for patients with leukaemia, when there is a high risk of cancer returning after moderate doses of chemotherapy. A quantity of bone marrow is removed from the patient, who then receives a high dose of chemotherapy, which destroys cancer cells and normal bone marrow cells. While this is happening, all cancer cells are removed from the extracted bone marrow sample. The 'cleaned up' marrow is then returned to the patient. This technique is relatively straightforward because there are no genetic differences between the marrow and the recipient.

THE CHANCES OF REJECTION

In some ways, stem cell transplant is like any other transplant: if there are genetic differences between donor and recipient, the transplant will be rejected. The potential for these differences are mainly in the HLA (human leucocyte antigen) genes: if donor and recipient have different tissue types, the recipient will reject the stem cell transplant. Therefore the same rules apply to stem cell transplant as any other transplant: transplants between identical twins will work well; transplants between siblings have a one in four chance of working

Milestones
IN MEDICINE

The largest stem cell registry in the UK is the Anthony Nolan Trust (www.anthonynolan.com). The Trust was established in memory of a boy who died over 20 years ago. The first stem cell transplant was carried out in 1973. Just a year later young Anthony Nolan was taken ill and needed a stem cell transplant. Unfortunately, no family member was a suitable HLA match, and at that time there was no registry of potential donors. Anthony was unable to have a safe transplant and died in 1979, aged seven. More than 300,000 donors have since registered with the Anthony Nolan Trust.

well – when the HLA types happen to be identical. The chances of a random donor having the same tissue type and the transplant working well are very small.

Graft versus host disease

Stem cell transplant differs from other transplants in that the immune cells will grow out of the donor stem cells. If there are genetic differences between the donor and the recipient, the new immune cells, derived from the donor, will attack tissues throughout the recipient's body. This is called graft versus host disease. Acute graft versus host disease happens very soon after the transplant and attacks numerous tissues throughout the body. Chronic graft versus host disease usually causes skin and lung problems several months after transplantation.

The risk of graft versus host disease is reduced by ensuring that donor and recipient have identical HLA (tissue) types, if possible. However, other genetic differences between the donor and recipient are likely, and cannot be predicted by tissue typing technologies, and so most stem cell transplant patients take immunosuppressive drugs to reduce the risk as much as possible.

Registering as a potential unrelated donor

The chances of someone who needs a stem cell transplant having an identical twin are very slim. The chances of having a sibling who can act as a donor are also low. As a result, unrelated donors are increasingly being used for transplants. However, unrelated donor stem cell transplant only works if there is an exact HLA match. Therefore, the more people register their HLA type with a stem cell registry, the more likely it is that someone in need of a stem cell transplant will find a successful match.

Donors need to be healthy and 18 to 40 years old. If a patient requires a transplant of a particular donor's HLA type, the donor is contacted and a blood sample is taken for a cross-match, to confirm that the risk of stem cell rejection or graft versus host disease is as low as possible. All being well, the donor's bone marrow is then removed and then transplanted into the recipient.

Banks for cord blood too

In the future, banks of cord blood may be used as a resource for children who need stem cell transplantation. Stem cells from cord blood are much less likely to cause graft versus host disease, but are only available in small numbers and so are not usually suitable for adult patients.

Stem cell gene therapy for SCID

Every year, a handful of boys are born with X-linked severe combined immunodeficiency (SCID). This condition means that they are quite unable to fight infections of any kind. Stem cell gene therapy could transform their life prospects.

WHAT IS X-LINKED SCID?

In X-linked severe combined immunodeficiency (SCID) there is a mutation, an incorrect DNA sequence, in the gene that codes for a protein – the common gamma (gc) chain. Without the gc chain, there are no T cells and no natural killer (NK) cells, both vital for fighting invading microorganisms. This means that babies born with X-linked SCID succumb to even the mildest infections. Untreated, they die of infections within their first year.

Even though B cells do develop, because the young patients lack the T cells that normally help B cells function properly, the B cells do not produce enough useful antibodies, further impairing the immune response.

LIFE IN A 'BUBBLE'

Standard treatment for children with SCID consists of lifelong injections of immunoglobulin (antibodies from donor blood), and stem cell transplantation if a tissue-matched donor can be found. To protect the patients from infection, they may at certain stages have to live in a sterile room – a so-called 'bubble' with filtered, cleansed air – and be given daily antibiotics. Parents must don sterile gowns and face masks and can have only minimal contact with their sick child.

THE NEW TREATMENT

The first step in the new stem cell gene therapy – developed by doctors in France and the UK – is to remove some of the child's bone marrow cells under general anaesthetic from the hip bone, using a needle and syringe.

In an incubator and under sterile conditions these bone marrow cells are mixed in a kind of plastic bag with growth factors that selectively stimulate the stem cells. A virus that carries the correct human form of the gc chain gene is added to these defective stem cells. The virus itself causes no harm, but delivers a normal gc chain gene to the stem cell nucleus, where it can take over from the defective gene and rescue the vital immune cell function. The process of selecting the cells and putting them in contact with the virus takes about three days, after which

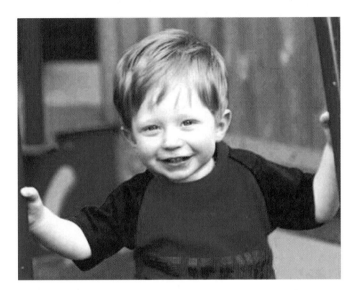

Ready to live a normal life for the first time
Rhys Evans from South Wales is one of the first children to have received stem cell gene therapy for SCID. He left London's Great Ormond Street Hospital in 2002 with the hope that he will be able to enjoy a normal childhood from now on.

about 20 million cells are put back into the patient by injection in a process that resembles a blood transfusion.

In most other transplant procedures the recipient's bone marrow must be emptied out to make room for donor cells; this is usually done by killing the recipient's cells with irradiation. The therapy being pioneered for X-linked SCID is quite different: bone marrow cells are already so sparse that there is no need to 'prepare' a patient to accommodate the corrected cells.

After receiving their modified stem cells, patients slowly acquire immune cells. T cells are usually detected in the blood four to six months after a stem cell transplant, but appear two to four months after stem cell gene therapy and are about three times as abundant. It has now been several years since the first young patients with X-linked SCID received stem cell gene therapy. So far, it appears that their immune systems have been successfully repaired. In the future, gene therapy may be adapted for other diseases caused by mutations, such as haemophilia.

Fighting childhood leukaemia

The outlook for children with leukaemia has never been better. Although it is often in children that leukaemia progresses most rapidly, more children than ever before now go into remission with the prospect of a healthy adult life.

A boy receiving chemotherapy for leukaemia plays cards with his mother.

The types of leukaemia to which children are most likely to fall victim are acute lymphoblastic leukaemia or acute myeloid leukaemia – usually aggressive, fast-growing tumours – or chronic myeloid leukaemia, which begins slowly but can transform into a much more aggressive disease.

In children the first signs are often loss of energy, tiredness and fever. There may be persistent infections, nosebleeds, bruising and aching joints or bones. The disease is usually diagnosed via a blood test and bone marrow biopsy.

Every year about 450 children are diagnosed with leukaemia in the UK. Of these, about three-quarters are cured (a remission of five years after treatment is generally considered as a cure). The reasons why medicine is now enjoying higher success rates against leukaemia in children are early diagnosis and more sophisticated treatment programmes. The principal weapons in medicine's fight against this disease are chemotherapy, radiotherapy and stem cell transplant.

Leukaemic blood cells

A coloured scanning electron micrograph (SEM) of the blood of a patient with leukaemia shows a typical overabundance of white blood cells. They form a marked contrast with the SEM of healthy blood shown below. The term leukaemia covers any of a group of cancerous diseases in which the overproduction of immature, abnormal white blood cells suppresses the production of red blood cells, platelets and normal white blood cells. This leads to a vastly increased susceptibility to infection, plus anaemia and problems caused by the blood not clotting properly. If leukaemia is not adequately treated, it will ultimately prove fatal.

Treatment options

How each case of leukaemia is treated varies from child to child, depending on factors such as the precise type of leukaemia, how aggressive it is and the success of any previous treatments.

CHEMOTHERAPY

With acute lymphoblastic leukaemia, chemotherapy treatment is started as soon as possible after diagnosis. This involves the injection into a vein of a cytotoxic (cell-poisoning) drug that will kill cancerous cells – but also some healthy cells as well. If the leukaemia returns, chemotherapy is given again, sometimes at a higher dosage.

RADIOTHERAPY

Radiotherapy may be used to kill any leukaemia calls that have spread into the fluid around the brain and spinal cord. It is sometimes given after chemotherapy to 'mop up' any cancer cells still remaining in this cerebrospinal fluid.

STEM CELL TRANSPLANTATION

When chemotherapy treatment destroys so many healthy cells in the bone marrow that the child's immune system has been severely damaged, stem cell transplantation (see page 120) is the treatment of choice to rejuvenate the immune system.

ISOLATION

Both chemotherapy (possibly coupled with radiotherapy) and stem cell transplantation can affect the immune system so badly that any infection can pose a danger to the patient. In these circumstances, the best protection for the patient is isolation in a sterile room within the hospital.

A child leukaemia patient in a sterile isolation room in a hospital, following chemotherapy and stem cell transplantation. The few people allowed into the room have to 'scrub up' and put on special clothing before entering.

A happy outcome

Joanne Mills – shown here, second from the left, standing next to consultant oncologist Dr Alison Leiper – was diagnosed with acute lymphoblastic leukaemia at the age of nine. Acute lymphoblastic leukaemia is the most common of all the cancers contracted by children. Joanne clearly remembers being whisked into London's Great Ormond Street Hospital for Children, where treatment was started immediately. The outcome was successful and she has been leukaemia-free ever since.

In the not-so-distant past some treatments for leukaemia could make it difficult for some patients to go on to have children in later life, but happily the situation is now much improved. Joanne is pictured here with her daughter and son.

Great Ormond Street Hospital for Children, founded in 1852, is the largest care centre in Great Britain for children with leukaemia, and one of the world's leading research centres in the field of child health. In 2002 Great Ormond Street Hospital and 21 other specialised paediatric oncology centres included within the UK Children's Cancer Study Group celebrated 25 years of increasing success in fighting childhood cancer. The number of children who develop cancer each year in the UK – approximately one in every 600, aged 15 or under – has remained constant for the last 25 years and longer, but cure rates for some cancers have almost doubled in that time, going from four out of ten to nearly eight out of ten.

Organ transplants and immunosuppression

The transplant revolution is relatively recent. The reason is that although the surgical techniques for transplanting organs have in some cases been known for some time, immunosuppression therapy that prevents organs being rejected has only got off the ground in the last 30 years or so.

Transplantation is the treatment of choice for patients with end-stage organ failure. Solid organs that may be transplanted include the kidney, the heart, liver, lungs, the pancreas and small bowel. The reason that kidney transplants are the most commonly performed is because living people (usually relatives) can donate one of their two healthy kidneys. In addition, patients with kidney failure can be kept alive on dialysis machines until an organ is available. Patients with severe heart, lung or liver failure are not so fortunate and need a transplant urgently.

HOW DEMAND OUTSTRIPS SUPPLY

In the UK from January to March 2002, 605 patients received organs from 205 organ donors. But there were still 5833 people registered as waiting for a transplant.

Most organs are from brainstem-dead cadaver donors. There are never enough cadaver donors, however – and the number is declining due to a fall in how many people are killed in road accidents and by intracranial bleeding.

Milestones
IN MEDICINE

1954 First successful kidney transplant, between identical twins in Boston, USA.

1963 Thomas Starzl carries out the first successful liver transplant, in Denver, USA.

1967 In Cape Town, South Africa, Christiaan Barnard performs the first successful heart transplant.

1967 First successful pancreas transplant.

1984 First heart-liver transplant is achieved, again by Thomas Starzl, in Pittsburgh, USA.

1990 First successful heart-lung transplant is performed.

1991 First successful small intestine transplant.

Increasing numbers of living kidney donors

Transplant numbers have been kept constant by an increase in the number of living donors. In the UK, for instance, there were just 89 living donor kidney transplants in 1991, compared with 358 in 2001 (18 per cent of all kidney transplants in the UK in 2001).

Live related donation can be very safe because a related donor is genetically similar or even identical to the recipient. It is also possible for an unrelated living donor to donate a kidney. This is less likely to be successful, because of genetic differences, and could possibly lead to organ selling, which is of course illegal in the UK.

MATCHING DONOR AND RECIPIENT

If a transplant is to be a success, it is essential that the donated organ is transplanted into a recipient with a compatible blood group. If not, the transplanted organ will be rejected. In addition, there is also a procedure called tissue typing, or matching, which examines the HLA profile of donor and recipient tissues to assess compatibility of their antigens.

There are protein chains called human leucocyte antigens (HLA) in almost every cell in the body. Everyone has a particular HLA type, known as their tissue type, inherited from their parents. We each have two HLA A antigens, two HLA B antigens and two HLA DR antigens; these are made up of one A, one B and one DR passed down from each parent. The function of HLA is to regulate the immune response. It plays a key role in enabling the body to distinguish self from non-self.

What is the importance of a close tissue match?

HLA matching is important in heart transplantation, but sometimes there is not enough time to perform a cross-match (a compatibility test). Many studies have shown there is no need to HLA match liver grafts.

With kidneys, however, the closer the HLA match between kidney donor organ and recipient, the greater the chance of a transplant being accepted by the recipient's body. There is a 25 per cent chance of two siblings sharing the same tissue type, a 50 per cent chance of siblings being a half match, and a 25 per cent chance of siblings being totally mismatched. Parents are a half match for their children, and children are a half match for their parents. There is only a small chance of an unrelated donor-recipient pair having a good HLA match.

WHY A LIVING DONOR IS PREFERABLE

- It takes less time to transplant an organ from donor to recipient – a matter of a few hours at most. This is because the operation can be planned well in advance, so that the pre-transplant tests that delay a cadaver donor transplant can be carried out in the days before the organ is taken from the live donor. The longer a kidney, for example, is kept on ice, the less likely it is that it will work at once. Immediate functioning is a major factor in successful organ transplant outcome.
- A living donor is given a thorough health check, something that is not possible with a cadaver donor.
- If a living donor is already lined up, a patient in need of a new kidney is more likely to receive a transplant before having to begin dialysis, which increases the chances of the transplant being a success.

DONATION AFTER THE DONOR'S DEATH

Usually, a cadaver donor has sustained irreversible brainstem death and subsequently been maintained on a ventilator machine. There are also 'non-heart-beating'

A quarter of the population of Great Britain and Northern Ireland carries a donor card.

donors who have not been given assisted ventilation (a machine has not been keeping them breathing); these are very rare at present in the UK.

Before the operation

Three conditions have to be met before cadaveric donation can take place.

- As is the case for blood donors, the donor must not have infections such as hepatitis or HIV, and must not have a life-threatening condition such as cancer.
- Very careful testing must confirm irreversible brainstem death (see page 128).
- There must be consent from the donor's family.

As soon as a family grants permission for a patient's organs to be used, the transplant coordinator liaises with intensive care staff, operating theatre staff and transplant teams to arrange a time for the donation, and blood is sent to a transplant laboratory to determine the patient's tissue type.

Harvesting the organs

Just before the operation begins, the cadaver donor is taken off the ventilator (if applicable). First the cardiac team retrieve the heart and lungs. It is important that these organs are transplanted within 12 hours of their removal from the donor. The liver is removed next; this should be transplanted as soon as possible. Then the kidneys and pancreas are taken out; the average time to a kidney being transplanted into a recipient in the UK is 17 hours.

Seeking permission from relatives
In the UK, relatives of someone who has just died and is a potential organ donor are always asked to consent to the donation of organs, whether or not the potential donor carried a donor card or joined a donor register. If the family of the donor refuse their consent, the donation does not take place.

IMMUNOSUPPRESSIVE THERAPY

The body's immune system naturally recognises transplanted organs as foreign and rejects them. For this reason, immunosuppression – interrupting this normal tendency – plays a major role in the success of any organ transplant.

The immunosuppressive regime has two critical phases: first the immediate post-implant phase, when it is necessary to prevent sensitisation of mature recipient cells capable of recognising the newly transplanted organ; and then cumulative unresponsiveness to the new organ, which develops as the recipient is continually exposed to donor HLA from the organ.

Currently there does not seem to be one best immunosuppressive regime suitable for all patients. As doctors learn more about individual immune responses it becomes possible to tailor specific immunosuppressive regimes to the needs of the individual patient. All the drugs listed below are still in use – in most cases patients are treated with a combination of two or three. One trend is that fewer steroids are being prescribed as more potent drugs become available.

Steroids and azathioprine

When transplantation surgery began to take off in the 1970s, the immunosuppression regime was limited to steroids and azathioprine. Steroids have a non-specific immunosuppressive effect, acting by damping down the inflammatory response. Azathioprine interferes with the metabolism of cells involved in the immune response, and stops them from proliferating.

Cyclosporin (CSA)

Cyclosporin (CSA) arrived on the scene in the early 1980s, and from the mid 1980s to mid 1990s – the 'cyclosporin era' – a great improvement was seen in graft survival figures. CSA acts by inhibiting the production of chemical signals which act between cells, thus preventing cells from proliferating. The earliest form of CSA was replaced in the late 90s by a more effective form marketed as Neoral, which has been shown to provide better overall immunosuppression. One drawback with CSA, however, is that in high doses the drug damages the kidneys – as shown by heart transplant patients who have gone into renal failure as a result of CSA treatment. CSA can also cause the gums to grow over the teeth (gum hypertrophy) and excessive hair growth (hypertrichosis).

How can we be sure a potential donor is really dead?

TALKING POINT

A common worry is whether a potential donor whose heartbeat and breathing have been maintained on a ventilator is actually dead. Any patient on life support who is identified as a potential donor must undergo a series of tests at two different times by a medical team other than the transplant team. Only if the patient is completely unresponsive in both sets of tests can the patient be diagnosed as brainstem dead.

Other immunosuppressive drugs

- Tacrolimus (FK506, Prograf) is derived from a fungus, like CSA, and has a similar mode of action, though it acts on a wider range of chemical signals. It too is nephrotoxic (damages the kidneys), but it doesn't cause gum hypertrophy or hypertrichosis. When it was first introduced, there was concern over the high incidence of diabetes caused, but with more widespread use and a better understanding of therapeutic blood levels, this has lessened. There is evidence that tacrolimus may be a better immunosuppressive agent than CSA after a liver transplant. Patients with severe CSA side effects can benefit from a switch to tacrolimus, and the drug is used as a 'rescue agent' when patients have rejection episodes not treatable by an increase in steroids.

- Sirolimus (Rapamycin) works by competing with the action of chemical signals on target cells and can be used in conjunction with CSA. Sirolimus works synergistically with CSA. Though sirolimus is not harmful to kidneys, it does cause high cholesterol levels. A large proportion of patients involved in sirolimus trials have had to be treated with lipid-lowering drugs.

- Mycophenolate mofetil (MMF, CellCept) inhibits chemical signalling by interfering with cell metabolism. UK trials showed a 50 per cent reduction in acute rejection when MMF was used in conjunction with CSA, and in the USA MMF has virtually replaced azathioprine in clinical practice. Use of the drug in the UK has been restricted by cost, but it is now effectively used in conjunction with steroids in patients with chronic CSA nephrotoxicity, and is considered to be of significant benefit in pancreas transplants.

• A monoclonal antibody (anti-CD3, OKT3) or a polyclonal antibody (anti-lymphocyte globulin, ALG, or anti-thymocyte globulin, ATG) is used to help patients experiencing a rejection crisis. These agents deplete the cells responsible for rejection, so a transplanted organ is not attacked. It's important that sufficient cells remain to guard against infection, so a balance is reached between preventing rejection and preventing infection.

SUCCESSFUL TRANSPLANTATION

Various factors influence whether a transplant will be successful and enable a return to a normal lifestyle. Donor factors that tip the balance in favour of a successful outcome include:

• normal anatomy of the donor organ;
• evidence that the organ was working well before donation;
• the donor was between 5 and 50 years old.

Donor factors that might lead to early failure of the transplant include:

• a lapse of time greater than 45 minutes from the point at which the donor's blood ceased to flow through an organ to the moment when the organ is perfused with solution and packed in ice – known as the 'warm ischaemia time'.

• a period of more than 24 hours from the time when the organ is first perfused and chilled to the moment when the recipient's blood begins to circulate within it – the cold ischaemia time.
• evidence of infection.

Recipient factors are just as important. Tipping the balance in favour of a successful outcome are:

• good HLA matching with the donor – especially HLA DR;
• lack of side effects from the immunosuppressants;
• compliance in taking anti-rejection drugs, maybe for life.

Recipient factors leading to early failure include:

• a previous transplant history and the formation of HLA specific antibodies;
• recurrent disease in the new organ;
• anatomical abnormalities which makes links between the donor and the recipient's blood vessels difficult.

Transplant recipients can return to a near normal life, a fact best exemplified by the Transplant Games. The quality of life should continue to improve for these patients as better immunosuppressants are developed, coupled with immunosuppressant regimes tailored to the individual needs of each recipient, and as understanding of the processes involved in rejection increases.

Transplant Games
The US Transplant Games take place biannually as a four-day athletic event and a celebration of how successful a treatment organ transplantation can be. In addition, the World Transplant Games are also held every two years.

Life on immunosuppressants

Immunosuppressant drugs are taken before and after organ and tissue transplants to prevent rejection. They do so by impairing the body's ability to fight infection. So how does this impact on everyday life for recipients, who often have to take these drugs for the rest of their lives?

Every patient's situation is slightly different, but in general someone on immunosuppressants can live a life as normal as anyone else, so long as certain basic precautions and common-sense procedures are followed.

All immunosuppressant drugs increase the risk of catching an infection, and of an infection doing greater harm to the body than if these drugs were not being taken. This is because these drugs impair the body's ability to recognise and respond to infection. In particular, immunosuppressants such as mycophenolate, azathioprine and sirolimus tend to suppress white blood cells, which normally help to fight infection. For this reason, doctors regularly monitor the white blood cell counts of patients on these drugs.

TIPS FOR AVOIDING INFECTIONS

There are various measures that can be taken to reduce the chances of catching an infection.

- **High hygiene standards** Practise good hand hygiene: wash hands frequently; avoid close contact with other people who may be carrying an infection; use gloves and a mask if having to handle pet wastes.
- **Keeping the doctor informed** Report to the doctor any contact with infectious illness, so that the appropriate preventative treatment can be prescribed. Typical examples include chickenpox and the herpes virus.
- **Vaccinations before holidaying abroad** Consult the doctor about which vaccines can and cannot be taken: for example, live vaccines (that is, measles/mumps/rubella, oral polio vaccine and yellow fever vaccines) should not be given to a transplant recipient.
- **Going to the dentist** Liaise with the transplant doctor and dentist before any dental procedures are performed to find out whether or not antibiotics are needed.
- **Food poisoning** Beware of food poisoning if you are on immunosuppressants, as food poisoning can have a more dangerous effect than it would otherwise. In particular, avoid any egg and cheese products that have not been completely cooked.

DEALING WITH AN INFECTION

Early detection of an infection is crucial to avoid complications. A doctor should be notified of any signs of infection such as a sore throat, a cough, swollen lymph nodes or mouth sores, so that the appropriate investigations and treatments can be started as soon as possible. Anyone on immunosuppressants should get immediate medical advice after an animal or insect bite, or after receiving a cut or wound of any kind.

The importance of exercise
Regular exercise will help to keep you healthy and ready to fight off infection. Low-impact, repetitive exercises such as walking and skipping are particularly good for the bones and a simple way to help keep the potential immunosuppressant side effect of osteoporosis at bay.

HOW TO KEEP SIDE EFFECTS TO A MINIMUM

The frequency and seriousness of the side effects of immunosuppressants are related to each drug's specific effect and the size of the dose. Some signs and symptoms can be seen or felt, while others are detected only by medical tests, so regular monitoring by a health professional is essential. The potential side effects of each immunosuppressive drug differ and will include only a few of the signs and symptoms referred to here.

- **Keep bones strong** The risk of osteoporosis can be minimised by taking vitamin D and calcium supplements as medically prescribed; adopting a diet with enough calcium and vitamin D; cutting down or quitting smoking and alcohol; and gentle weight-bearing exercises.
- **Avoid high blood pressure** Reduce or eliminate risk factors such as high cholesterol, high salt intake, smoking and obesity. A diet high in fruit and vegetables and low in salt, sugar and fat is best. Take blood pressure medicines precisely as directed by the doctor.
- **Minimise swelling** A mild accumulation of fluid in the body can often be alleviated by a few common-sense measures, such as drinking lots of water so fluid is encouraged to pass through the body; reducing salt intake; increasing physical activity;

avoiding tight clothes, jewellery and shoes; elevating the feet whenever possible – by raising the foot of the bed, for example.
- **Bruising** Bruising can be avoided by careful blood monitoring by the doctor. Patients should immediately report bruising in unusual areas, such as the chest, inner thighs or inner arms.
- **Avoid high lipid (fat) levels (hyperlipidaemia)** The presence in the blood of an abnormally high concentration of fats often occurs with immunosuppressant use, and increases the risk of heart disease. The doctor can help by keeping a regular check on blood lipid levels and by prescribing medicines called 'statins' to control cholesterol levels. Patients can help by exercising regularly and

adopting a low-fat, low-cholesterol diet.
- **Tremors** Report any tremors to the doctor immediately so the cause can be identified and the right treatment set in place. Sometimes, simple stretching exercises are enough to temporarily relieve the problem.
- **Conquer headaches** Paracetamol is safe for transplant patients to take. By contrast, ibuprofen (Nurofen, Advil) and naproxen (Naprosyn) can reduce kidney function and should be avoided by transplant recipients. Report any severe or persistent headaches to the doctor immediately.
- **Maintain hair condition** Hair can be weakened and may even break off at the roots. Help hair to stay healthy by avoiding perming or colouring, and covering the hair when sunbathing or swimming.
- **Skin care** Wear sunscreen and protective clothing in the sun. Notify the doctor at once if any moles change in any way.
- **Gums** Careful attention to dental hygiene is the way to help avoid overgrown or bleeding gums.

Removing the spleen

An operation to remove the spleen is called a splenectomy. This is sometimes performed on people who have a severely enlarged spleen (splenomegaly). More often, however, the spleen is removed because it has been ruptured following an accident.

The spleen has two major roles in controlling infection.
- It acts as a filter to remove bacteria from the blood.
- It contains special B cells which make antibodies against bacteria, for example against pneumococcus, which can cause serious infections including pneumonia.

A lot of blood flows through the spleen and if it is even slightly damaged following physical injury, there can be massive internal bleeding. In this emergency situation, a surgeon may decide it is better to remove the spleen rather than attempt to repair it.

The operation

A surgeon may opt to remove a spleen by traditional surgical methods, or by using the newer techniques of laparoscopic 'keyhole' surgery. Before the operation begins tests will have been carried out to find out as much as possible about the spleen's condition – in particular, the extent of any trauma or enlargement. The patient is given antibiotics just before the operation to cut down on the risk of infection.

After the operation

Patients can manage quite well without a spleen, but are left more prone to infection than before. The risk of sepsis from bacterial infection is greatest among children, and so a splenectomy should be avoided if at all possible if the patient is a child.

Splenectomy patients can develop severe septicaemia after even quite trivial infection, such as a splinter in the finger: patients can become severely ill in just a few minutes. For this reason, all splenectomy patients should wear an alert bracelet or tag. Even more importantly, patients who have had a splenectomy should take simple antibiotics such as penicillin daily. In the USA, patients are recommended to take penicillin for the first few years after the operation; in the UK, splenectomy patients are often advised to take penicillin for the rest of their lives. Additionally, splenectomy patients need to be vaccinated against pneumococcus and meningococcus (which can cause septicaemia) in order to encourage the immune system to make antibodies.

Laparoscopic splenectomy (spleen removal)

a Guided by video images from the laparoscopic camera, the surgeon inserts a cutting tool through a small incision in the abdomen, and with this cuts the ligaments and other tissues that attach the spleen to the diaphragm, stomach and colon.

b The splenic artery and splenic vein – the major blood vessels – are tied off and cut. Bleeding is stopped by electrocautery or stitches, whichever is most appropriate.

c The spleen is pushed into a bag and is cut into pieces so it can be retrieved via a small incision in the abdominal wall.

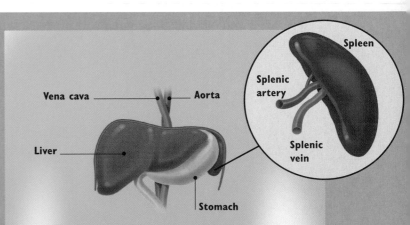

Vena cava · Aorta · Spleen · Splenic artery · Splenic vein · Liver · Stomach

a — Liver · Stomach · Spleen · Ligament · Cutting tool

b — Splenic artery · Spleen · Splenic vein

c — Spleen in retrieval bag

A to Z

OF DISEASES AND DISORDERS

This section gives information on the main illnesses and medical conditions that affect the blood and immune system.

This index is divided into two sections: Symptoms, and Diseases and disorders. Within these divisions, entries are arranged alphabetically and each is structured in a similar way:

What are the causes?

What are the symptoms?

How is it diagnosed?

What are the treatment options?

SYMPTOMS

ANAEMIA
A reduction in the amount of oxygen-rich haemoglobin in the blood.

Haemoglobin in the blood gives a healthy colour to the skin. Sometimes anaemia is suggested by a pale appearance but many white people have a naturally pale complexion because there is less pigment in their skin, so the mucus membranes of the mouth and the whites of the eyes are better places to look for the pallor of anaemia.

What are the causes?
Anaemia can be caused by an iron or vitamin deficiency, blood loss or chronic illness. It can also be genetic in origin, or a side effect of certain medications.

How is it diagnosed?
The most usual symptom is fatigue, regardless of how much sleep and rest the patient is getting. If the anaemia is more severe, the patient may feel the heart beating inside the chest (palpitations) or have shortness of breath. It is important to remember, however, that these symptoms can also be caused by other medical problems.

The doctor will examine the patient and take account of the symptoms. A full blood count (p. 105) will then be taken to confirm the anaemia; this may also give clues to the cause of the anaemia.

What are the treatment options?
The type of treatment will depend on the underlying cause of the anaemia and therefore varies greatly from case to case (p. 114).

BLEEDING
Any excessive bleeding should make you think of getting medical advice.

What are the causes?
Excessive bleeding can occur if there are problems in the relevant organ. For example, heavy periods can indicate a hormonal imbalance or the presence of fibroids. Nosebleeds can indicate infections in the nose, or there may be a problem with the blood-clotting system. Bleeding can also occur in people who have been prescribed too many anticoagulants, such as warfarin.

How is it diagnosed?
In the case of a problem with the blood-clotting system there may be bleeding from several sites, for example from the gums as well as nose bleeds. In other instances, the bleeding may not be immediately obvious: in the eye it can impair vision, and bleeding into joints causes pain and swelling. These symptoms could mean that either the platelets (as in immune thrombocytopenia) or the clotting proteins (as in haemophilia) are not working.

What are the treatment options?
First, the bleeding must be stopped. Taking iron tablets is usually sufficient to replace red blood cells lost due to bleeding, but in the most severe cases a blood transfusion may be needed.

BRUISING
Bruises are areas of bleeding into the skin and are perfectly normal after bumps and injury to the skin.

What are the causes?
Most healthy children get bruises from time to time from heavy duty playing. In the elderly, bruising can occur because of the looseness of the tissues under the skin.

Excessive bruises can occur when there is no clear-cut history of trauma. They can sometimes happen in infections, such as meningococcal meningitis, so if a child or teenager (those most commonly affected by this disease) develops small bruises in the skin, fever and headache, it is important to get immediate medical advice. Abnormal bruises also occur when the clotting system is not working (see Bleeding).

What are the treatment options?
Elevation and an ice pack may help in cases where the cause is a trauma. Arnica cream is reputed to lessen the severity of bruises if applied immediately after a trauma. Otherwise, treatment depends on the cause of the bruising.

FEVER
This means raised temperature and is usually associated with specific diseases.

Normal temperature for most people is 37°C (98.6°F), although some people have a normal temperature about 0.5°C (1°F) higher.

What are the causes?

Fever usually indicates infection and develops as the body's immune system attempts to fight the infection. In children, temperature can rise rapidly; in adults, it may not rise so much but can cause more discomfort.

How is it diagnosed?

Raised temperature and feeling hot are the most common symptoms. Feverish people are often sweaty and have shivering attacks. Fever may cause fits in children.

Fever should be confirmed by taking the patient's temperature with a thermometer. The infectious cause of fever is often obvious, as with a sore throat or cough with sputum production, for example. Sometimes, however, the cause is not immediately obvious and in these cases blood and urine tests and perhaps X-rays may be required. Occasionally, a fever can be an early symptom of lymphoma or cancer.

What are the treatment options?

Treatment depends on the cause of the fever, but drinking plenty of fluids and taking aspirin will usually be the first treatment advised. If the cause is a specific disease, such as measles, treatment will be appropriate for the disease.

LYMPHADENOPATHY

Swelling of the lymph nodes, or glands, which are scattered through the body.

Lymph node swelling is an important clinical sign that always needs investigating, especially if it has persisted over several weeks (that is, has become chronic). The lymph nodes are quite near the surface in the neck, armpits and groin and can easily be felt when enlarged. Deeper lymph nodes are found in the chest and abdomen; enlargement of these nodes may be detected by X-ray or scanning techniques.

What are the causes?

Lymph nodes may be swollen in four different situations.
• Acute infection Lymph nodes are the manufacturing site for lymphocytes, the white cells that form a crucial part of the immune system. When an infection occurs, for example a sore throat caused by a viral infection, the local lymph nodes swell up. This happens because white cells take small samples of the virus to the lymph nodes in the locality to stimulate lymphocytes. Lymphocytes

that recognise the specific virus will respond by dividing to produce many more virus-specific lymphocytes. The process is organised by specialised lymphocytes known as helper cells (CD4 cells). The new lymphocytes created in the process may produce antibodies (B cells) that will help to kill the infection. Other specialised lymphocytes (cytotoxic cells) also help to kill viruses. In the case of a viral sore throat, lymph nodes in the neck swell up because of all the new cells produced.

In these situations there may be an increase in the number of lymphocytes in the blood, as the immune system throughout the body becomes activated. The immune system is capable of dealing with most infections very quickly, and usually the lymph node swelling settles after a few days and further investigation of acutely swollen lymph nodes is not necessary.
• Chronic infection Some infections are not easily cleared by the immune system. For example, the bacteria that cause tuberculosis evade the antibodies and cytotoxic cells produced by the immune system. HIV infection, too, cannot easily be cleared. In both these situations, lymph node swelling will persist for weeks or months. In the case of HIV infection, an HIV test will produce a diagnosis. In the case of tuberculosis, biopsy of the lymph nodes may be the only way of confirming the cause of the problem.
• Cancer The immune system's response to cancer can be a bit like its response to infection. White cells take samples of the cancerous cells to the local lymph nodes and the immune system tries to find cells that are capable of killing them. In breast cancer, for example, this results in the lymph nodes in the armpits swelling up as they try to respond to the cancer. In this case, a lump in the breast is usually present, and both the lump and the lymph nodes are removed by surgery.

In other cases, for example with throat cancer, the primary cancer may be hard to detect, and chronically swollen lymph nodes in the neck may be the first sign. Doctors can diagnose throat cancer by biopsying the swollen nodes, as well as by examining the inside of the throat.
• Lymphoma and leukaemia The lymphocytes of the immune system itself can occasionally become cancerous, causing either lymphoma or leukaemia. Swollen lymph nodes can occur anywhere in the body and gradually enlarge over several months. In this case, there are no signs of primary infection or cancer, and lymph node biopsy may be the only way of making the diagnosis.

THROMBOSIS
The blocking of a blood vessel by a blood clot, or thrombus.

What are the causes?
Abnormal blood clotting is sometimes a consequence of diseases of the blood vessels, generally the arteries. The arteries are usually damaged by atheroma (arteriosclerosis), caused by smoking, diabetes, high blood pressure or high cholesterol levels. When arteries are blocked by thrombosis, the local tissues are unable to get enough oxygen and will eventually die. This can cause clots in the brain (stroke), the heart (coronary thrombosis, myocardial infarction) or the legs (gangrene).

Blood clots in the veins are often caused by an increase in the tendency of the blood to clot, for example in women taking the contraceptive pill or during pregnancy. Blood also has a tendency to clot if you are immobile for too long. This is the cause of the so-called 'economy class syndrome' and of clots after operations.

Blood clots in veins generally start in the legs, where they cause pain and swelling in the calves; this is referred to as a deep venous thrombosis (DVT). Sometimes these clots break off and travel through the veins to the lungs. Big clots can then damage the blood supply to the lungs, leading to breathlessness, coughing up blood and pains in the chest.

How is it diagnosed?
A doctor may diagnose superficial clots from a description of the discomfort and an examination of the skin. DVT can be diagnosed either by ultrasound or through injecting a contrast dye into a large vein in the foot or ankle. An X-ray may then detect clots.

What are the treatment options?
During prolonged periods of immobility, such as after surgery, or when someone is on a long flight, clotting can be prevented by exercising the legs regularly. If correctly used, elastic stockings can help to make clotting less likely.

A superficial clot may respond positively to heat, elevation, and aspirin or NSAIDs. DVT is normally treated by injection of an anticoagulant, such as heparin, to prevent clots from growing. After heparin treatment, warfarin may be prescribed for several months to thin the blood. Sometimes, a drug to dissolve the clot is needed. Support tights may be recommended to prevent swelling and reduce the chances of complications.

TIREDNESS
This is the normal response of the body to an excess of activity – physical or mental – and not enough sleep.

It can be very difficult to distinguish normal tiredness from excessive tiredness. People who are tired even after eight hours sleep every night may have an underlying problem.

What are the causes?
Fatigue is common in people who have infections and it may take several weeks to get over the excessive tiredness caused by a bad case of flu. Many diseases can cause excessive tiredness, and it is often seen in people who have anaemia, arthritis and cancer. If these diseases are ruled out, the tiredness may be caused by chronic fatigue syndrome (p. 140), also known as myalagic encephalitis.

One in five men and one in three women admit feeling tired 'most of the time'.

How is it diagnosed?
Patients with chronic fatigue syndrome may also have pains in the muscles, sore throats and other symptoms.

What are the treatment options?
Once the underlying cause has been established, the appropriate treatment can be determined.

WEIGHT LOSS
The loss of more than two or three kilograms (five to seven pounds) in weight can suggest that there may be underlying disease.

What are the causes?
Psychological issues or problems with either the upper or lower parts of the gastrointestinal tract can all cause weight loss. If none of these is present, weight loss may be the result of a wide range of other disorders including hormone problems, infections and tumours.

Loss of appetite is common in upper gastrointestinal tract diseases and psychological disorders. If the patient has persistent diarrhoea, it may suggest problems with the lower intestinal tract.

What are the treatment options?
Treatment will depend on the underlying cause of the weight loss.

DISEASES AND DISORDERS

ANTIBODY DEFICIENCY
A lack of adequate antibodies to protect the body from disease.

Antibodies are proteins produced in the blood to counteract the effect of toxins produced by bacteria.

What are the causes?
Particularly in older people, antibody deficiency can be caused by an underlying disease, for example chronic lymphocytic leukaemia or myeloma. It can also be genetic in origin, in which case it can affect young people. Whatever the cause, the consequences are the same.

What are the symptoms?
Antibodies are most important in protecting the airways, from the nose to the lungs. These parts of the body are particularly exposed to bacteria and viruses in the air. People with antibody deficiency tend to suffer repeated infections of the airways, resulting in runny noses, sinusitis (the sinuses are air spaces in the skull on either side of the nose), sore throats and chest infections. After one infection has cleared, another soon follows. Bouts of pneumonia are common, and some patients have infections of the bones or joints, or meningitis.

How is it diagnosed?
Antibody deficiency is easy to diagnose by checking the patient's immunoglobulin levels (p. 110). Unfortunately there is often a delay of several years before the correct diagnosis is made.

What are the treatment options?
Immunologists usually look after patients with antibody deficiency, since treatment can be quite complicated and is likely to be required for the remainder of the patient's life. Some people with mild forms of the illness respond well to lifelong antibiotics. Other sufferers need to have immunoglobulin replacement therapy. Immunoglobulin can be extracted from donor blood and needs to be given by injection; it can be given intravenously, usually every three weeks, or into the skin (subcutaneously) once a week. This treatment is continued for the rest of the patient's life. To make the treatment more convenient, patients may be trained to give themselves immunoglobulin at home.

Antibody deficiency can be one type of primary immune deficiency, along with severe combined immunodeficiency (SCID, see p. 151), complement deficiency and chronic granulomatous disease. In the UK, the patients' organisation the Primary Immunodeficiency Association has a web site (www.pia.org.uk) that is well worth consulting.

AUTOIMMUNE DISEASES
In autoimmunity, the immune system attacks the body's own cells and tissues.

There are many different autoimmune disorders, including some of the most common diseases. Some important ones are shown below; many of these are mentioned in sections of this book or in other books in the series.

The purpose of T cells and B cells in the immune system is to attack bacteria, viruses and other alien microbes that enter the body. The immune system has mechanisms for preventing it from attacking normal components of the

Autoimmune diseases

DISEASE	WHAT IS ATTACKED BY THE IMMUNE SYSTEM
Type I diabetes	Insulin secreting cells in the pancreas
Thyroid disease (Graves' disease, Hashimoto's disease)	Thyroid gland
Immune thrombocytopenia (ITP)	Platelets in the blood
Rheumatoid arthritis	Joint linings and other tissues
Systemic lupus erythematosus (SLE)	Joints, skin, kidneys
Pernicious anaemia	Cells lining the stomach
Coeliac disease	The lining of the small intestine
Multiple sclerosis	White matter in the brain and spinal cord

body. As T cells and B cells develop, they are 'educated' – in the thymus and bone marrow respectively – not to attack normal body tissues. When this training process goes wrong, autoimmune diseases develop.

What are the causes?

The training process can go wrong for genetic reasons, so autoimmunity often tends to run through families. It is not unusual, for example, for one sibling to have thyroid disease and another to have diabetes. Sometimes the abnormal genes can cause an unlucky person to have more than one autoimmune disease. Other factors, such as infections and sometimes drugs, can trigger autoimmunity in people who have the relevant genes.

How is it diagnosed?

Autoimmune diseases are diagnosed by investigations which show that organs being attacked are not working. For example, in pernicious anaemia it is possible to show that the gut is not absorbing enough vitamin B_{12}. It is then also possible to show that the immune system is making antibodies against the stomach lining cells that enable the absorption of vitamin B_{12}. These autoantibody tests are available for many autoimmune diseases.

What are the treatment options?

For some diseases, it is simplest to replace the products of the tissues that have been damaged by the immune system. For instance, diabetic patients may be given insulin, and people with autoimmune thyroid disease may be given the thyroid hormone thyroxine. In other cases, it is necessary to prevent the immune system from causing further damage. This can be done using immunosuppressive drugs, which try to 'switch off' the immune system. These include steroids (prednisolone), azathioprine, infliximab, methotrexate and cyclosporin. Each of these drugs has a range of side effects, but they all switch off the normal immune response to bacteria and viruses. Patients who are on these drugs are therefore at higher risk of infection.

BLEEDING DISORDERS
These disorders occur when the mechanisms for making the blood clot are not working.

What are the causes?

Platelets are small cells in the blood which glue together whenever a blood vessel is damaged – as when the skin is

cut, for instance. If there are insufficient platelets in the blood, the blood will not clot. This can happen if the bone marrow has been damaged so that not enough platelets are being produced, for example in leukaemia. It can also happen when platelets are destroyed by diseases such as immune thrombocytopenia, ITP (p. 146).

Proteins in the blood also help the blood to clot during injuries. These proteins, called clotting factors, are produced mainly in the liver, so if there is severe liver disease the blood will not clot.

Some men are unable to produce one clotting factor, Factor VIII, because they have inherited an abnormal gene for the protein; this is known as haemophilia (p. 144). Without treatment, these men bleed too heavily.

Alternatively, the clotting factors can be triggered abnormally by infections. Clotting then takes place in healthy, uninjured blood vessels. All the clotting factors are then used up and there is bleeding elsewhere.

How is it diagnosed?

Platelet deficiency can be diagnosed by doing a full blood count, and all these problems can be diagnosed by means of a clotting screen.

What are the treatment options?

Drugs can be administered to control excessive bleeding in some patients; others need transfusions of plasma products. Life-long treatment is normally required.

BONE MARROW FAILURE
The bone marrow is a factory for producing blood cells. Its failure is defined as an inability to produce adequate numbers of blood cells.

Bone marrow produces neutrophils (for fighting infection), red cells (for carrying oxygen around the body) and platelets (which help the blood to clot). Every day the bone marrow stem cells divide to produce many billions of each cell type. If the bone marrow is damaged, it cannot produce the necessary blood cells.

What are the causes?

Damage can be caused by diseases of the bone marrow cells, such as leukaemia, lymphoma or other cancers; in these cases the normal marrow is simply squeezed out by the malignant cells. In other cases, the marrow fails because it is damaged by drugs, radiation or the immune system.

This can be referred to as aplastic anaemia, which occurs as a result of an autoimmune attack on the marrow.

Drug damage is the commonest cause of bone marrow failure. It can happen as a result of cytotoxic chemotherapy drugs used to treat cancers, when the risk of bone marrow failure is related to the dose of chemotherapy given. This is because these drugs aim to prevent cells from dividing, making damage to bone marrow is almost inevitable.

Very rarely, other drugs, for example some antibiotics, can cause bone marrow failure. Such reactions are very unlikely and are totally unpredictable. Finally, exposure to chemicals, including benzene, insecticides and heavy metals, may cause bone marrow failure.

What are the symptoms?
Anaemia, frequent infections and unexplained bleeding are all symptoms of bone marrow failure.

How is it diagnosed?
Bone marrow failure may be suggested by a full blood count test. To be absolutely certain that this is what is wrong when a patient shows very low blood counts, the bone marrow must be examined. This is done by bone marrow aspiration, which involves removing a little marrow fluid via a needle, for microscopic evaluation.

A bone marrow biopsy (also called a bone marrow trephine, see p. 108) may be performed at the same time as bone marrow aspiration. Whilst bone marrow aspiration involves sucking out bone marrow, a bone marrow biopsy involves taking out a core of bone marrow and solid bone. The biopsy provides additional useful information regarding possible abnormalities in the bone marrow that are not always revealed by aspiration. A biopsy may show cancer cells, when these exist. In the aplastic anaemia types of problem (due to drugs, chemical or autoimmune disease), it is possible to see that there is a massive reduction of the blood-manufacturing cells.

What are the treatment options?
Because of all the complications, bone marrow failure is a serious problem. Patients are usually admitted to hospital so that they can be closely monitored. Patients with a very low neutrophil count, for example, need to have their temperature taken frequently, since a raised temperature is one of the earliest signs of infection.

If there is evidence of cancer, this must be treated. Exposure to drugs and chemicals that cause bone marrow failure must be checked. If there is evidence of an autoimmune attack on the marrow, immunosuppressive drugs may be given.

Much of the treatment of bone marrow failure is supportive. For example, blood transfusions can be given to relieve the symptoms of patients with severe anaemia, and platelets can be given to people who are bleeding because of low platelet counts. The hope is that whatever caused the bone marrow to fail in the first place will improve. When improvement is very unlikely, stem cell transplant may be carried out, provided there is a suitable donor available (p. 120).

BURKITT'S TUMOUR
A particular kind of tumour of the B cells, Burkitt's tumour also belongs to the group of non-Hodgkin's lymphomas.

This disease has a higher incidence in equatorial Africa than in the rest of the world, and it was in Africa that surgeon Dennis Burkitt first noted that the tumour often occurred in the jaw. In the rest of the world it is usually first found in the abdomen.

What are the causes?
This tumour is commonly associated with the presence of the Epstein-Barr virus, a kind of herpes virus that causes glandular fever (infectious mononucleosis, p. 147) and which most people harbour; the tumour is more common in children than in adults. Why it can occasionally cause cancer is not known.

What are the symptoms?
A tumour on the jaw causes pain and swelling and loosening of the teeth; an abdominal tumour causes local pain and swelling. Spread to other sites may be rapid.

How is it diagnosed?
Diagnosis will be confirmed by biopsy of the lump and examination of the biopsy tissue under the microscope. This will reveal the characteristic diffuse malignant B cells, which do not look like normal B cells.

What are the treatment options?
Burkitt's tumour responds well to chemotherapy and prolonged remissions can be achieved with this kind of treatment. Facial tumours tend to respond rather better than abdominal tumours. Surgery is also an option.

CHRONIC FATIGUE SYNDROME
Extreme tiredness, which does not improve with sleep and is made worse by physical or mental exertion.

This condition is also called myalagic encephalitis (ME).

What is the cause?
The cause of chronic fatigue syndrome (CFS) is not known. Because the illness has been found to affect people in clusters, for example groups of people working at the same place, some researchers have thought it is triggered by a specific infection. However, no triggering infection has been found consistently in everyone suffering from CFS. The idea that infection may cause CFS has led some doctors to think that the immune system is involved in causing the symptoms of CFS. To date, however, there is no evidence of immunological problems in all patients with CFS.

HELP YOUR DOCTOR TO HELP YOU

Choosing a CFS support group

Because chronic fatigue syndrome is so poorly understood, it's important to find a doctor who is sympathetic and informed, if you are diagnosed with the condition. Many sufferers also find joining a support group useful. Most support groups are free, or charge only a small membership fee. A good support group should:

- *Be well established, with a track record of meeting its members' needs.*

- *Include people whom you feel comfortable with, who will neither dominate discussions nor keep silent.*

- *Have a good mix of the newly diagnosed and those with longer standing illness, so that there is a wealth of different experiences and perceptions on which to draw.*

Groups to avoid, on the other hand, include those which:

- *Advocate that you stop taking prescribed medication.*

- *Offer a quick fix to the problem.*

- *Try to persuade sufferers to purchase 'miracle' cures.*

What are the symptoms?
The most obvious symptom of chronic fatigue syndrome is extreme tiredness, but many patients have other symptoms, such as muscle pain or sore throats, which may develop after an infection and tend to last many months or even years. Although many people with CFS become depressed, the current thinking is that this is a result, not the cause, of all the other symptoms. In other words, CFS is not primarily a psychological illness.

How is it diagnosed?
There is no specific test for CFS. The diagnosis is made in patients who have all the symptoms with no other explanation for them. For example, it is important to rule out anaemia as a cause of chronic fatigue.

Many patients with CFS feel that the medical profession does not take their symptoms seriously, and one of the best things that can happen to CFS patients is to find a medical team that believes their symptoms are real and wants to try to improve them. Patients also find it helpful to be told that in most cases their symptoms will improve over time.

What are the treatment options?
Because we do not understand what causes CFS, there is currently no cure. Treatment aims to improve the fatigue, usually by encouraging people to gradually build up their tolerance of exercise. Patients may be given a series of graded exercises which they build up over several weeks or months. For example, they may be asked to walk 50 metres (150ft) a day in the first week, 100 metres (300ft) a day the second week and so on.

Because depression is such a common part of CFS, many patients also benefit from input from psychologists or, sometimes, antidepressant drugs.

CHRONIC GRANULOMATOUS DISEASE
A rare type of inherited immune deficiency affecting the neutrophils – blood cells that fight infection.

What is the cause?
Patients suffering from chronic granulomatous disease (CGD) are able to make neutrophils – the most prevalent white blood cell type – but the neutrophils are usually unable to kill bacteria. Normally, a few neutrophils are recruited to the site of an infection by immune system signals, and they then kill the bacteria. Once the neutrophils have done their work, they die.

What are the symptoms?
Once the immune system is responding to infection, pus (an accumulation of dead neutrophils) is usually produced in small amounts at the site of the infection. In CGD, because the neutrophils are unable to kill the bacteria, they continue to accumulate and a large amount of pus is formed, resulting in an abscess.

How is it diagnosed?
Confirmation of the diagnosis is by specialist laboratory analysis, which looks at the function of the blood cells and the cells' metabolism.

What are the treatment options?
Patients with CGD are given antibiotics to clear and/or prevent infections. Stem cell transplant and gene therapy are currently being tested as treatments of CGD.

COMPLEMENT DEFICIENCIES
A rare type of inherited immune deficiency.

Complement is blood protein, which plays a role in the immune system's fight against infection. Some people inherit mutations in their complement genes, making them very prone to infections, particularly types of meningitis. Some people with complement deficiencies are also more likely to develop the autoimmune disease systemic lupus erythematosus, SLE (p. 154).

What are the symptoms?
Symptoms depend on the specific complement deficiency. Some people remain symptomless. Those who suffer from frequent infections may develop fever, headaches, diarrhoea and chest pain. If an autoimmune condition develops, a patient may lose weight, and suffer from a rash and joint pain. Other symptoms include pain, swelling of the face and lumps on the skin.

How is it diagnosed?
Blood tests measure the activity of the complement system, and identify those parts that are not working properly. Specific tests for the individual components of the system are then carried out, as well as a white blood cell count.

What are the treatment options?
At present, there is no way to cure complement deficiency. Any resulting infections can be treated with antibiotics, and

patients can be vaccinated to reduce the risks of diseases such as flu and pneumonia. A bone marrow transplant is appropriate in some cases.

Some patients remain healthy; others suffer frequent infections requiring hospital stays. Those with autoimmune diseases could have a normal life expectancy, but some types of complement deficiency have a high death rate, with few patients still alive ten years after diagnosis.

DIABETES MELLITUS
A condition in which glucose is not broken down to produce energy due to a lack of the pancreatic hormone insulin, or an inability of the tissues to respond to insulin's effects.

This relatively common condition results in persistently high levels of glucose in the blood, since the cells are unable to absorb glucose from the bloodstream as they normally would. When the sugar level becomes very high, there can be damage to the blood vessels (atheroma, arteriosclerosis), increasing the risk of problems such as stroke, gangrene and coronary thrombosis. The high blood sugar level also damages the eyes and kidneys.

There are two types of diabetes, type I and type II. The cause of a case of diabetes is usually not known.

Type I diabetes
This is an autoimmune disease. Like other autoimmune diseases it tends to run in families and usually starts in children, who rapidly become ill. They lose weight dramatically, and if they are not treated with insulin will go into a coma. When a patient first becomes ill, there are signs that the body is producing antibodies that act against the islet cells in the pancreas that normally secrete insulin. These antibodies can be tested for in the laboratory. The immune attack on the pancreas doesn't take long to destroy the islet cells; once this happens, the antibodies disappear.

Type II diabetes
This type of diabetes affects older people. Various factors as well as increasing age put people at risk; obesity is thought to be a major factor in the development of the disease and affected individuals are usually overweight. This form of the disease is not thought to be autoimmune, but also tends to run in families. People with type II diabetes are still able to produce some insulin, unlike those with type I diabetes.

What are the symptoms?

Type I diabetes usually appears suddenly, with children complaining of excessive thirst and dry mouth; there is excessive urination, dramatic weight loss and possibly coma.

Type II diabetes is often only picked up when sugar is detected in the urine or raised sugar levels are detected in the blood. Patients may complain of a lack of energy and simply feeling off-colour.

How is it diagnosed?

Diagnosis is usually made on the basis of raised glucose levels in the blood.

What are the treatment options?

Individuals with type I diabetes need insulin treatment for life. This involves injections, which patients are taught to give themselves, often several times a day. Immunologists are looking at other ways of preventing or treating this type of diabetes. If a patient is diagnosed before the islet cells are destroyed, it is possible that immunosuppressive drugs may prevent the disease; this has been tested in clinical trials. While children are on immunosuppressive drugs, diabetes can be prevented. However, as soon as the drugs are stopped (which they have to be eventually, because of potential side effects) the immune system starts attacking the pancreas and diabetes develops. Another immunological treatment is a pancreas transplant. This is being tested in trials on patients who already have diabetes.

Many patients with type II diabetes do not need insulin injections. Instead, the condition is controlled by sticking to a low-sugar diet, losing any excess weight and/or taking tablets to lower the blood sugar levels. The outlook for these patients is good.

GLANDULAR FEVER
See Infectious mononucleosis, p. 147.

GRAVES' DISEASE
Autoimmune disease that causes overactivity of the thyroid gland – hyperthyroidism.

What are the causes?

In Graves' disease the immune system makes antibodies against the thyroid gland, stimulating it to secrete increased amounts of thyroxine. The thyroid gland is not damaged by this process but it does become larger than normal.

What are the symptoms?

The thyroid overactivity causes weight loss and restlessness. A special characteristic of patients with Graves' disease is that they have very prominent eyes. This happens because of a build-up of tissue behind the eyes, not because the eyes are swollen.

Graves' disease affects only 0.25 per cent of the population overall, but is eight times more common in women than men.

How is it diagnosed?

Graves' disease is diagnosed by performing thyroid function tests and tests of autoimmunity.

What are the treatment options?

Treatment consists of anti-thyroid medication to reduce the activity of the thyroid gland.

HAEMOLYTIC ANAEMIAS
Anaemias resulting from haemolysis – the excessive destruction of red blood cells.

Red blood cells have only a limited life span of about 120 days. When they are showing signs of damage, they are taken up by cells in the spleen and destroyed. The body recycles some of the valuable components of the red cells, such as iron, while others, for example the yellow pigment bilirubin, are disposed of in the liver.

A number of different mechanisms can damage red cells, and the damage may be great enough to destroy those in the circulation, or cause them to be taken up by the spleen.

What are the causes?

Haemolysis can be caused by certain genetic diseases, by some infections, such as malaria, or by the immune system attacking the red blood cells.

- **Hereditary spherocytosis** In this genetic disease, the red cells have an abnormal shape and form spheres instead of discs. The spleen takes up all the sphere-shaped red cells so sufferers have bouts of anaemia.
- **Sickle cell disease** This is another inherited problem that can cause anaemia (p. 134).
- **Malaria** Here, the parasite lives inside the red cells. As it grows, it damages the red cells, which are eventually destroyed in the circulation of blood in the spleen.
- **Blood of the wrong group** If the wrong type of blood is given during a transfusion, antibodies will bind on to the

red cells and activate the complement, a constituent of the blood (p. 141). One of the roles of complement is to punch holes in invading bacteria, but if complement is activated in the vicinity of red cells, it punches holes in those. The cells rapidly burst and there are two major consequences: firstly, there are fewer cells to transport oxygen around the body, resulting in anaemia; secondly, the cells' contents are also released into the circulation, where they can cause damage, including kidney failure.

- Haemolytic disease of the newborn This is similar in some ways to a transfusion of the wrong blood. The red cells are the unborn baby's own cells and the antibody, which in this instance comes from the mother, is nearly always against the Rhesus system.
- Auto immune haemolytic anaemia It is possible for the immune system to attack the body's own normal red blood cells in a form of autoimmunity. Effects can be dramatic if the cells are destroyed rapidly in the circulation. More frequently, there is a gradual attack on the red cells, which are prematurely taken up by the spleen. Autoimmune haemolytic anaemia can occur as a result of other diseases – for example, it is sometimes seen in cases of chronic lymphatic leukaemia (p. 148), or systemic lupus erythematosus, SLE (p. 154). Sometimes drugs, such as penicillin, can trigger autoimmune haemolytic anaemia.

What are the symptoms?

Symptoms of haemolysis are the same as those of anaemia: fatigue, breathlessness and palpitations. The patient may be very pale or slightly jaundiced. In this case, the jaundice is due to excessive amounts of bilirubin in the bloodstream and not liver disease. Some patients, particularly those with autoimmune haemolytic anaemia, have an enlarged spleen.

How is it diagnosed?

A diagnosis of haemolytic anaemia is suggested by finding reduced haemoglobin levels in the blood count. Sometimes the blood film (p. 105) is very useful. For example, in hereditary spherocytosis the abnormal sphere-shaped red cells are apparent. In cases where the immune system is attacking red cells, the Coombs' test (p. 106) will show that antibodies are binding on to cells.

What are the treatment options?

The treatment of haemolytic anaemia depends on the cause. When there is severe haemolysis, it is important to keep the patient well hydrated so that the toxic substances released during destruction of the red cells are passed out through the kidneys. If the anaemia is severe, it may be necessary to give a blood transfusion; this is done with great care.

In the hereditary disorders (but not sickle cell disease) it may be necessary to remove the spleen by surgery (a splenectomy) to control the anaemia. The decision to do this always has to be balanced against the risk that the body will lose some of its ability to fight infection.

In cases of autoimmune haemolytic anaemia, immunosuppressive drugs may be given. If these do not work, sometimes it is necessary to remove the spleen.

HAEMOLYTIC DISEASE OF THE NEWBORN

In this disease, a pregnant woman's immune system attacks the baby's red blood cells, causing severe anaemia.

For this to happen, the mother and baby must have different Rhesus blood groups: the mother must be Rhesus negative and the baby Rhesus positive because it has inherited the positive gene from its father.

What are the causes?

The Rhesus positive gene makes the baby's red cells different from the mother's. If a few of the baby's red cells leak across into the mother's circulation during pregnancy or labour, her immune system will recognise them as being different and will start making antibodies. These antibodies usually do not cause problems for the first Rhesus positive baby, but if the mother becomes pregnant with another Rhesus positive baby, the amount of antibodies increases. These will cross the placenta into the baby's circulation, and the unborn child's red cells are attacked as a result.

What are the symptoms?

The baby is born severely anaemic and a positive result in a Coombs' test (p. 106) will indicate that the baby's red cells have been attacked by antibodies.

What are the treatment options?

A severely anaemic baby may require an exchange blood transfusion, in which the baby's blood is exchanged with fresh blood. Anaemia in the newborn can, however, be prevented. Only a minority of women are Rhesus negative and they can be identified by blood group testing during pregnancy. After each baby is born the mother can be given an injection of Anti D, which works by rapidly destroying any red cells from the baby that have leaked across into the mother's circulation. Once these are destroyed, the mother's immune system will no longer be stimulated to make anti-Rhesus antibodies.

HAEMOPHILIA
An X-linked inherited disorder of the clotting system that only affects males.

What are the causes?
Haemophiliacs have a mutation in the gene for Factor VIII, one of the proteins that normally helps the blood to clot. (See also X-linked disorders, p. 155.)

What are the symptoms?
Because of this disorder of the clotting system, haemophiliacs tend to bleed heavily after even minor injuries. Most of this bleeding takes place internally, often into joints. Over the years, this damages the joints and haemophiliacs can end up very disabled.

How is it diagnosed?
Haemophilia is easily diagnosed by doing a clotting screen and then measuring the levels of Factor VIII.

What are the treatment options?
Haemophilia is treatable with Factor VIII. Patients are usually trained so that they can give themselves Factor VIII intravenously at home.

Factor VIII can be extracted from donated blood, but in order to manufacture sufficient Factor VIII, blood from many different donors must be pooled. This carries a risk of spreading infections by blood-borne viruses, particularly HIV and hepatitis C, which attacks the liver. In the early 1980s, many haemophiliacs across the world were infected with these viruses, but since the mid-1980s, blood has been tested for HIV and tests for hepatitis C were introduced in the 1990s. Factor VIII manufactured from donated blood should now be much safer.

Factor VIII can also be manufactured using DNA technology. The human gene for Factor VIII is inserted into bacterial cells, which then produce Factor VIII protein; this technology produces Factor VIII that is free from the risk of infection. Known as recombinant Factor VIII, this type is very expensive, but haemophilia organisations across the world are trying to make sure that patients receive it.

HASHIMOTO'S DISEASE
In contrast to Graves' disease, this autoimmune disease causes underactivity of the thyroid — hypothyroidism.

Hashimoto's disease is a typical autoimmune disease. In this case, the immune system attacks the thyroid gland, resulting in its gradual destruction.

What are the symptoms?
The thyroid gland may initially be swollen. Underactivity of the thyroid causes weight gain and decreased energy.

How is it diagnosed?
Hashimoto's disease is diagnosed through doing thyroid function tests and autoimmunity tests.

What are the treatment options?
Treatment consists of thyroxine tablets to replace the hormones that the thyroid should be making. Medication and regular blood tests should keep symptoms under control and mean that there are no long-term effects.

HIV INFECTION/AIDS
HIV is the virus that can cause AIDS — acquired immunodeficiency syndrome.

The HIV (human immunodeficiency virus) epidemic started in the 1980s, when it received considerable publicity. AIDS may have dropped out of the headlines in the West, but it has not disappeared: over the past ten years it has killed tens of millions of people and orphaned millions of children.

What are the causes?
The HIV virus infects and damages the T helper cells – known as the CD4+ cells – in the immune system. These cells, which coordinate the immune response to bacteria, viruses, parasites and cancer, have been described as the conductors of the immunological orchestra. When T helper cells are not working, the immune system is unable to respond to infections and cancers.

HIV spreads from person to person only after intimate contact. This usually includes penetrative vaginal or anal sex between men and women or men and men. HIV can also be spread by drug users who share needles, and can be passed from mother to baby in the womb, during childbirth or by breastfeeding. HIV is now rarely spread by blood transfusions.

What are the symptoms?

The majority of people do not even notice if they have been infected with HIV, but in 10 per cent or so of patients there can be a shortlived illness, with sore throat, fever and rashes. HIV takes a long time to damage the T helper cells. Typically it is five years or so before the infected patient notices any symptoms at all.

Early symptoms of immune system damage caused by HIV infection include fungal infections of the mouth and severe attacks of herpes or chickenpox. Other patients notice weight loss and lymphadenopathy – swollen lymph nodes (p. 135).

Specific infections and cancers are characteristic of AIDS. As the immune deficiency worsens, more severe infections occur. These include specific types of chest infection, for example pneumocystis pneumonia and tuberculosis. Later on, vision may be damaged by a virus called CMV, and the parasite *Toxoplasma gondii* may cause toxoplasmosis, which can lead to brain abscesses. The severe immune system weakness may allow cancers to grow unchecked. These include non-Hodgkin's lymphoma and a skin cancer known as Kaposi's sarcoma. As time goes by, it is usual for patients to have several different infections and possibly one of the forms of cancer.

Nearly one-third of all adults in the USA and Europe have antibodies to Toxoplasma, which means they have been exposed to this parasite.

How is it diagnosed?

Blood tests can show if HIV is active and damaging the immune system. The viral load test is a type of polymerase chain reaction (PCR) test (p. 109) which measures how actively HIV is dividing, and CD4 counts show how much damage HIV has done to these cells. Over the years, the viral load tends to increase and the CD4 count falls.

What are the treatment options?

Each of the individual infections and cancers can usually be treated. Once an infection has been cleared, patients remain on antibiotics to prevent the infection coming back, as it will very likely do when the immune system is weakened. When a patient has several different infections at the same time, treatment becomes much more difficult.

The best way to treat HIV infection is to prevent the damage from occurring in the first place. Anti-retroviral drugs (p. 112) prevent HIV from going through its life cycle and damaging T helper cells. These drugs can be taken once the viral load is showing signs of high HIV activity and the CD4 count is beginning to fall.

One problem with HIV is that the virus mutates continuously. It is possible for it to become resistant to the anti-retroviral drugs. Patients usually take a combination of three, or even four, different anti-retroviral drugs because the chances of the virus becoming resistant to three or four different drugs at once is less likely than to one drug alone.

Millions of dollars have been spent on vaccine research for HIV, so far without much success. One reason is that there is no suitable animal on which vaccines can be tested. In the past, vaccines have been tested initially on animals and then tried out on humans. Chimpanzees are the only animals other than humans that are attacked by HIV, but scientists and others are reluctant to see chimpanzees used in vaccine experiments because they are a protected species.

Another problem is that there are many hundreds of strains of HIV. Because the virus mutates so quickly it is highly likely that an HIV strain from Africa would be very different from a strain from Europe. A vaccine that works for an African strain would probably not work for a European strain, and vice versa.

What is the outlook?

People infected with HIV may remain well for ten years or more, but at present it is thought likely that the vast majority, if not all, will eventually develop AIDS. Long-term use of recently introduced drugs may improve this outlook. Improvements in treatment of infections, as well new drugs, mean that many people remain physically and mentally healthy for years after AIDS has been being diagnosed.

HODGKIN'S DISEASE

A tumour of the lymphatic tissue, which is classified separately from other non-Hodgkin's lymphomas (NHL).

Hodgkin's disease (HD) is more common in males than females. It occurs mainly in young adults, with a second peak in middle age.

What are the causes?

The cause is unknown. An association with the Epstein-Barr virus (which causes glandular fever) has been suggested but not unequivocally proven.

What are the symptoms?

A patient with HD may have painless swollen lymph nodes, possibly associated with general tiredness, fever, itchiness, night sweats and weight loss. Generalised itching or pain in enlarged lymph nodes after drinking alcohol is also an occasional symptom. A common site for an HD tumour is in the chest, between the lungs, and this may cause a cough or painful breathing.

How is it diagnosed?
Investigations to confirm HD include:
- A blood test, which may show anaemia. The test will also check for other diseases that may cause swollen lymph nodes, such as glandular fever.
- A bone marrow biopsy, done to exclude other haematological disorders, but HD is rare in bone marrow.
- A chest X-ray, which will show any swollen nodes in this region. Swollen nodes will be biopsied and examined for the presence of cells characteristic of HD.

What are the treatment options?
Depending on the stage the disease has reached, treatment will be either radiotherapy alone or radiotherapy with chemotherapy. The management of Hodgkin's disease is one of the success stories in cancer research and most cases can now be cured. However, this success has been tempered by the discovery that the high-dose therapies needed to cure this disease may actually cause secondary malignancy, such as leukaemia, later in life. One aim of cancer therapy research is to tailor the treatment dose according to the volume of disease, cell and cytogenetic subtype. It may then be possible to reduce the chances of the therapy causing another cancer, while also avoiding an underdose, with potential for relapse.

IMMUNE DEFICIENCIES
Although there are many types of immune deficiencies, they all result in vulnerability to infection.

Immune deficiencies can be caused by relatively rare genetic problems, such as severe combined immunodeficiency (SCID, p. 151), chronic granulomatous disease (CGD, p. 140) and complement and antibody deficiency. Immune deficiencies can also be caused by drugs; for example, most cases of neutropenia (a decrease in the number of neutrophils in the blood) are caused by cytotoxic drugs used for cancer treatment. Immunosuppressive drugs used to treat autoimmune disease or to support organ transplantation also

More than 80 immunodeficiency diseases are currently recognised by the World Health Organisation.

cause immune deficiency, but the biggest cause worldwide is HIV infection (p. 144).

What are the treatment options?
Some types of immunodeficiency respond to treatment with intravenous gammaglobulin (IVIG); in others stem cell transplant may be an option. Antibiotics are prescribed to treat the recurrent infections.

IGA DEFICIENCY
This is the most common antibody deficiency.

IgA is the antibody found in all body secretions: for example in saliva, in the bowels, tears and mucus in the chest. IgA in breast milk is an important source of antibodies for babies. IgA deficiency is not life-threatening, but people who do not produce IgA may have a higher risk of infections of the chest and intestine.

IMMUNE THROMBOCYTOPENIA
An autoimmune bleeding disorder, immune thrombocytopenia leads to destruction of the platelets in the blood.

Platelets are the blood cells that play a part in the blood clotting process following injury. If the platelets are being destroyed, there is a tendency for bleeding to take place. Patients with immune thrombocytopenia (ITP) make antibodies against their own platelets. The spleen is responsible for clearing old red cells, white cells and platelets from the blood. In ITP, the platelets coated with antibodies are destroyed by the spleen.

What are the causes?
There are two main types of ITP. In children, the disease tends to be triggered by infection. Childhood ITP may be quite severe, but after a few weeks the platelet count generally returns to normal.

Adult ITP tends to be a long-lasting disease, which may continue for the rest of the patient's life. Sometimes patients have an underlying problem, such as SLE (p. 154) or chronic lymphocytic leukaemia (p. 148).

What are the symptoms?
Patients with ITP first notice abnormal bruising or bleeding. The doctor may notice that the spleen is enlarged.

How is it diagnosed?

The low numbers of platelets in the blood can be diagnosed by a full blood count. Sometimes a bone marrow examination needs to be done to confirm that the problem is due to destruction of platelets rather than impaired production of platelets, which is part of bone marrow failure (p. 138).

What are the treatment options?

There are many different treatments for ITP. If the platelet count is very low or if the patient has serious bleeding, it is possible to give platelet transfusions from donated blood. More usually, treatment aims to stop platelet destruction by using immunosuppressive drugs (see autoimmune diseases, p. 137), intravenous immunoglobulin (see antibody deficiency, p. 137) or Anti D injections (see haemolytic disease of the newborn, p. 143). In some cases, ITP cannot be controlled by these measures and the removal of the spleen is the only way to stop it destroying platelet cells.

INFECTIOUS MONONUCLEOSIS
Commonly known as glandular fever, this is a viral infection.

What are the causes?

The Epstein-Barr virus, one of the herpes viruses, is the cause of infectious mononucleosis. It commonly affects children and young people aged between 15 and 25. It is not particularly infectious and is contracted by intimate contact, such as kissing, with someone infected with the virus, which is carried by a large percentage of the population. The incubation period can be as long as six weeks after infection.

What are the symptoms?

The disease usually starts with a sore throat and fever, tiredness and a feeling of being unwell. The lymph nodes in the neck, armpits and groin become swollen. Sometimes there is a rash. In severe cases, the spleen may be enlarged. On the other hand, many people who become infected with the Epstein-Barr virus experience no symptoms at all.

How is it diagnosed?

The doctor takes account of all the symptoms and a blood test confirms the diagnosis by showing the presence in the blood of antibodies to the Epstein-Barr virus, and also characteristic B cells.

What are the treatment options?

The patient can take painkillers to relieve fever and pain, but rest is generally all the treatment that is needed. Most people recover fully within four to six weeks, although a feeling of fatigue can persist for several weeks longer.

LEUKAEMIA
Cancer of the white blood cells, which can affect any of the white blood cell types.

Lymphoblastic leukaemia is cancer of B or T lymphocytes or their precursor cells (immature B or T cells). Myeloid leukaemia is cancer of another type of cell produced in the bone marrow, for example neutrophils.

Children are mainly affected by acute lymphoblastic leukaemia (ALL) or acute myeloid leukaemia (AML), which are usually aggressive, fast-growing tumours if untreated, and by chronic myeloid (or myelogenous) leukaemia (CML), which begins as a slowly progressing disease but usually terminates with an acute phase. The most common leukaemias found in adults are AML and chronic lymphocytic leukaemia (CLL), a type which has a much slower course. All leukaemias affect the bone marrow (where cells are usually first seen). CLL can affect the lymph nodes and is thus similar to lymphoma.

What are the causes?

The cause of leukaemia is known only in a small number of instances. Some cases of T cell leukaemia are induced by a virus, Human T cell Leukaemia Virus-1 (HTLV-1), which is rare outside Japan and the Caribbean. Acute myeloid leukaemia may be caused by high doses of chemotherapy and radiation that have been given as treatment for previous cancers such as Hodgkin's disease.

What are the symptoms?

In children, the first signs may be loss of energy, tiredness and fever. There may be persistent infections, nosebleeds, bruising and aching joints or bones. Adults suffer gradual or rapid weakness, fever and night sweats, as well as loss of weight and appetite. Bruising of the legs and arms may be common, the gums may bleed and women may have heavy periods. The lymph glands become swollen.

How is it diagnosed?

A diagnosis of leukaemia and identification of its subtype will be made from a blood test and a bone marrow biopsy.

A blood film and bone marrow smear will usually clearly show the morphology (shape and features) characteristic of the malignant cell type. If leukaemia in the cerebro-spinal fluid is suspected, a spinal tap will be carried out under local anaesthetic and some fluid drawn by syringe from the sheath surrounding the spinal cord. Bone marrow will also be analysed by a geneticist to determine whether the leukaemia cells have an abnormal chromosome pattern.

What are the treatment options?
It is important to find out which cell type is leukaemic and whether there is a particular chromosomal pattern, since both these factors have an influence on the treatment that will be given. Flow cytometry (p. 107) both confirms leukaemia (by measuring different proteins on the surface of cells) and monitors how many leukaemic cells are in the blood or bone marrow. A major advance in research has been the recognition of varying responses to treatment and differing treatment requirements according to the genetic abnormalities of the leukaemia subtype. Polymerase chain reaction (PCR) technologies are used to do this (p. 109).

ACUTE LYMPHOBLASTIC LEUKAEMIA
This is the most common childhood cancer, with the highest incidence at about five years of age. It is rare after the age of 15. This cancer is characterised by excess numbers of immature lymphocytes (a type of white cell) in the bone marrow and blood. In most cases the cell involved has features of a B and T cell precursor (a cell that, in normal development, could turn into either a B or a T cell) and most of the remaining cases are T cell leukaemias.

What are the causes?
Often no cause can be identified; the cancer does not appear to be genetic in origin.

What are the symptoms?
Symptoms include tiredness, weight loss, fever, bleeding gums and unusual bruising. Bone and joint pain, and possibly abdominal pain caused by an enlarged spleen may also be noticeable. As the normal balance of immune cells is upset in this disease, signs of infection may also be present. If the leukaemia has reached the cerebro-spinal fluid, additional symptoms may be headache and nausea.

How is it diagnosed?
Samples of blood and bone marrow will be taken, from which the haematologist will be able to identify the leukaemic cell type and the geneticist will be able to show whether there is a significant chromosome abnormality present which may influence the treatment.

What are the treatment options?
Treatment with chemotherapy is usually started within a couple of days of diagnosis. Blood and bone marrow samples will be taken regularly to check that the treatment is appropriate. The cure rate for children is now excellent. If the leukaemia does return, chemotherapy is given again, perhaps more intensively, and is sometimes followed by stem cell transplantation.

ACUTE MYELOID LEUKAEMIA
This is cancer of an immature bone marrow white cell type. It is less obviously age related than acute lymphoblastic leukaemia, and anyone may be afflicted, from the very young to the elderly.

What are the symptoms?
Symptoms are usually tiredness, fever and weight loss. There may also be bleeding from the gums and bruising anywhere on the body.

How is it diagnosed?
The doctor will take account of the symptoms, and arrange for blood and bone marrow tests. These will reveal the type of white cell involved and whether there is a particular chromosome abnormality. From this information, the haematologist or oncologist will make a decision as to the type of treatment to be given. The presence of certain chromosome changes in the leukaemic cells indicates a statistically better or worse prognosis.

What are the treatment options?
The initial treatment is chemotherapy, although sometimes this is not enough to control the leukaemia, and stem cell transplantation must then be carried out. Acute myeloid leukaemia can actually be caused by high-dose chemotherapy or radiation given as treatment for previous cancers such as lymphoma. This potential has been recognised relatively recently, and now high-dose regimens are given only when this is unavoidable.

CHRONIC LYMPHOCYTIC LEUKAEMIA
This type of leukaemia, which affects the lymphocytes in the blood and in the lymph nodes, is most common amongst older people.

What are the causes?

The causes of most cases of chronic lymphocytic leukaemias (CLL) are unknown. A minority of cases of CLL involving T cells are caused by a virus called HTLV-1, which is relatively common in Japan and the Caribbean. HTLV-1 is a distant cousin of HIV. Both viruses infect T cells, but the big difference is that HIV destroys T cells (eventually causing AIDS) while HTLV-1 makes T cells malignant and they then increase in number.

What are the symptoms?

In many patients chronic lymphocytic leukaemia does not show any symptoms at all; in others it causes swollen lymph nodes or spleen, and fever. Sometimes CLL causes a secondary immune deficiency, with antibody deficiency (leading to chest infections) and impaired T cells (leading to problems such as shingles). CLL can also cause an autoimmune attack of the red cells and platelets; it is one cause of immune thrombocytopenia, ITP (p. 146). Unlike other leukaemias, full-blown bone marrow failure is rare in cases of CLL.

How is it diagnosed?

The first step in the diagnosis of chronic lymphocytic leukaemia is the discovery of a raised lymphocyte count, as part of the full blood count. The CLL may turn up as an unexpected diagnosis when the blood count is done for other reasons, however – for example, before an operation. The lymphocyte count can also be raised in cases of infection, and the haematologist needs to distinguish these from CLL. This distinction is usually made by flow cytometry (p. 107).

Generally, lymphocytes responding to an infections are a mixture of B and T cells. In CLL, the situation is quite different. In about 95 per cent of cases of CLL, all the cells will be either B cells or T cells. Flow cytometry is so good at diagnosing CLL that often bone marrow testing is not required for this type of leukaemia. Flow cytometry can also count the number of malignant cells, so it is possible to assess a patient's response to treatment.

What are the treatment options?

About half of all cases of chronic lymphocytic leukaemia are discovered when a blood count is done for another reason; in these cases patients do not present any symptoms and often no treatment is required. For patients who do experience symptoms, courses of steroids can be helpful even if the leukaemia is not cured.

CHRONIC MYELOID LEUKAEMIA

This is cancer of the immature white cells that produce neutrophils. It can affect people of any age.

What are the causes?

Chronic myeloid leukaemia (CML) can occur after radiation or after administration of chemotherapy to treat another form of cancer. In most cases of CML, characteristic damaged chromosomes are present. These are referred to as the Philadelphia chromosome, and the genetic mutations that occur as a result are the cause of CML. When CML switches to a more aggressive form, more mutations or chromosomal damage are usually seen.

What are the symptoms?

Symptoms of enlarged spleen (splenomegaly, see p. 153) or bone marrow failure (p. 138) are common. The bone marrow failure may be quite mild, with modest fatigue,

What makes cancer cells so different from other cells?

Malignant cells differ from normal healthy body cells in two crucial characteristics. Firstly, they are monoclonal – that is, all the malignant cells in a single tumour are genetically identical. Genetic changes make the malignant cell inclined to keep dividing and producing many more malignant cells. Secondly, they are immortal. Most cells have a specific life span: for example, neutrophils survive for only a few days, then inbuilt mechanisms kill the cells. In malignancy, genetic changes affect the mechanisms that control the life span of the cell. For example, the chromosomal damage (called the Philadelphia chromosome) that causes chronic myeloid leukaemia makes the cells immortal, able to continue dividing and multiplying indefinitely.

Several genetic changes, or mutations, are usually required to make cells malignant. Sometimes there is a genetic basis for these changes, which is why some cancers run in families. For example, some individuals inherit an inability to repair defects in DNA. Infections may be involved in making cells malignant: the Epstein-Barr virus is implicated in lymphoma and the *Helicobacter pylori* bacterium has been linked to stomach cancer, for example.

ASK THE EXPERT

for example, being a symptom of anaemia. CML has a tendency to transform to a more aggressive disease, similar to acute myeloid leukaemia.

How is it diagnosed?
Chronic myeloid leukaemia is suggested by finding a very high neutrophil count in a blood sample, and on a blood film the neutrophils look abnormal. Bone marrow examination may be required. Cytogenetic testing of blood or bone marrow will probably show the Philadelphia chromosome in the majority of cases.

What are the treatment options?
Chemotherapy is used to treat CML. Frequently, strong chemotherapy followed by a stem cell transplant is needed, but treatment can only slow the disease, not cure it.

LYMPHOMA
A solid cancer of the lymphocytes, different from leukaemia (which can be thought of as liquid cancer in the blood).

Lymphoma generally occurs in the lymph nodes, the home of lymphocytes, but since lymphocytes can move around, it can occur anywhere in the body. There are various types of lymphoma. Hodgkin's disease (p. 145) is one major type; all the others are referred to as non-Hodgkin's lymphoma (NHL) or simply as lymphoma. Burkitt's tumour (p. 139) is a special kind of non-Hodgkin's lymphoma.

The incidence of NHL is increasing steadily, through its rise in frequency in patients on immunosuppressive drugs or with HIV. The normal immune system can recognise and kill lymphoma cells; when the immune system is damaged by HIV or drugs, lymphoma can then occur.

What are the symptoms?
The first indication of NHL is usually a lump or swollen painless lymph gland. This may be accompanied by weight loss, tiredness and unusual sweating at night.

How is it diagnosed?
If the doctor suspects NHL, the patient is referred to hospital for a biopsy of the lump or lymph gland. A piece of the lump is taken under general anaesthetic, or a needle biopsy is performed. The lump is then tested for signs of abnormal cells. A blood test is also done and a sample of bone marrow taken to check if the lymphoma is present in the marrow. CT or MRI scans are done to see if the lymphoma has spread to other parts of the body. If NHL is confirmed, the extent of the disease will be determined, and the stage of the disease designated on a scale of one to four.

What are the treatment options?
Chemotherapy and radiotherapy are generally used to treat lymphoma. Complete cure is possible for some people; in other cases treatment relieves the symptoms and can prolong life for several years.

MYALAGIC ENCEPHALITIS (ME)
See Chronic fatigue syndrome, p. 140.

MYELOMA
A cancer of specialised B lymphocytes known as plasma cells that tends to affect elderly people.

Normally, plasma cells secrete antibodies (also known as immunoglobulins) and play a key role in protecting against infection. In multiple myeloma, monoclonal plasma cells secrete only one kind of antibody and grow uncontrollably, taking over the bone marrow.

What are the causes?
The cause is uncertain, although since myeloma tends to run in families there may be a genetic element to it.

What are the symptoms?
Myeloma starts in the bone marrow and as it spreads causes widespread bone damage, bone pain and fractures. Useful antibody production is impaired, and sufferers are prone to infections such as chest infection.

How is it diagnosed?
When myeloma is suspected, electrophoresis (the study of the movement of charged particles such as proteins) is carried out to see if there is abnormal immunoglobulin in the blood or urine. A bone marrow examination is required to confirm the diagnosis.

What are the treatment options?
Some myelomas grow very slowly and require no treatment. Other more serious cases require chemotherapy; this may suppress the myeloma for several years or, sometimes, cure it.

NON-HODGKIN'S LYMPHOMA
See Lymphoma, p. 150.

PERNICIOUS ANAEMIA
An autoimmune disease that results in a deficiency of vitamin B$_{12}$ and anaemia.

What is the cause?
Vitamin B$_{12}$ is present in a wide range of foods so it is unusual for deficiency to result from a lack of vitamin B$_{12}$ in the diet. However, vitamin B$_{12}$ is not easily absorbed from the gut. Stomach cells called gastric parietal cells help to absorb the vitamin by secreting a protein known as intrinsic factor. In pernicious anaemia, the immune system makes antibodies that kill off both gastric parietal cells and intrinsic factor, blocking normal absorption of the vitamin.

What are the symptoms?
Patients with pernicious anaemia are usually anaemic (p. 134). Sometimes, because B$_{12}$ is required by the nervous system, they may have pins and needles or loss of balance.

How is it diagnosed?
A full blood count will show that the red cells are abnormally large. The diagnosis is confirmed by low levels of vitamin B$_{12}$ in the blood as well as antibodies against gastric parietal cells and intrinsic factor.

What are the treatment options?
Vitamin B$_{12}$ injections, given every month or so throughout the patient's life, ensure a good outlook.

RAYNAUD'S PHENOMENON
A painful condition that can occur when the hands or feet become very cold.

What are the causes?
This condition is due to poor blood supply to fingers and toes. In the cold, arteries constrict, making the problem worse. Rarely, the condition can be caused by underlying disease, such as myeloma (p. 150), in which blood can be so thick and sticky that it can't flow into the fingers, or SLE (p. 154), in which blood can't flow normally through inflamed arteries. The condition is a common side effect of beta blocker drugs used for high blood pressure. Women are particularly susceptible to mild Raynaud's phenomenon.

What are the symptoms?
The hands and toes turn very pale and become painful when cold; in severe cases the fingers or toes may go blue. When the patient warms up again, the fingers and toes turn red and may throb or tingle. In extreme cases, the blood supply becomes so damaged that the tissue in the fingers and toes may die and become gangrenous. In most cases of Raynaud's phenomenon, however, although the condition can be distressing, it does not cause gangrene.

How is it diagnosed?
A blood test will be taken to rule out any underlying disease. A normal protein electrophoresis (p. 110) will be used to check for myeloma, while a normal autoantibody test will eliminate the possibility of SLE.

What are the treatment options?
Medications that dilate blood vessels, such as calcium channel blockers, are often effective in treating the condition. But prevention is the best option: patients should avoid exposing the fingers, toes and face to the cold. Wearing gloves, warm socks and boots outdoors should help. Oven gloves can be used when taking food from the fridge or freezer. Sufferers should get help to stop smoking, if necessary, since smoking also causes arterial disease. In extreme progressive cases, an operation to cut the sympathetic nerves may be done, but this provides relief for only a year or two.

SEVERE COMBINED IMMUNODEFICIENCY (SCID)
This is not a single deficiency, but a group of inherited immunodeficiencies, affecting babies.

What are the causes?
There are about ten different known genetic causes of SCID. Some are X chromosome linked, which means that the defective gene can be passed from the mother; others are autosomal recessive: that is, both parents must carry the gene to pass the condition to their offspring. The mutations that cause SCID all affect proteins that are normally found in T cells.

What are the symptoms?
Babies with SCID become ill very soon after birth. They have no T cells and so are vulnerable to the same range of infections as patients with AIDS. They develop infections

and rashes and fail to put on weight. These symptoms can be very vague, and so are not always recognised quickly by doctors.

How is it diagnosed?
SCID can be rapidly diagnosed by doing a full blood count, which will show that the number of lymphocytes is very low. Then a T cell count will be done; it usually shows that there are no T cells in the blood.

What are the treatment options?
Babies with SCID need to be protected from infections. In the past, they were kept in large plastic 'bubbles' to protect them – the celebrated 'boy in the bubble' was a child with SCID. These days, with a better understanding of the problem, antibiotics can be given to prevent infections for several months at a time and bubbles are no longer required. Nonetheless, babies with SCID need to be given a new immune system if they are to survive. This can be done by stem cell transplant, but only if there is a suitable donor. An alternative is gene therapy, which has been successfully used for one form of SCID – gamma chain deficiency.

SEPTICAEMIA
Previously known as blood poisoning, septicaemia is a condition in which bacteria grow in the blood.

What are the causes?
Bacteria should never be present in the blood; if they are, the body's defences must have been damaged. Septicaemia commonly occurs when skin is damaged by severe burns, reflecting the skin's role as the biggest barrier to infection.

Septicemia also happens if parts of the immune system are impaired. The cells responsible for clearing bacteria from blood are called phagocytes. These cells literally eat up bacteria and then kill them; they include neutrophils that circulate in the blood, and other cells in the spleen.

Phagocytes can be damaged in different ways – many of them medically induced. For example, if the neutrophil count is very low (neutropenia), often as a result of chemotherapy for cancer, septicaemia can complicate what normally would be trivial skin infections. Such patients are usually given advice on avoiding infections and told to seek help quickly if they develop early symptoms of septicemia. If the spleen is removed, there is also a very high risk of septicaemia; indeed, the risk is so great that patients are often advised to stay on antibiotics for life.

What are the symptoms?
The symptoms of septicaemia include fevers, sweats and and shivering. Septicaemia damages the body's mechanism for maintaining blood pressure, and as blood pressure falls, the patient may lose consciousness and the kidneys may fail.

How is it diagnosed?
Blood cultures to confirm that bacteria are actually growing in the blood can be done, but septicaemia needs to be diagnosed quickly.

What are the treatment options?
As soon as septicaemia is suspected, intravenous antibiotics are urgently given to control the infection. Special measures, including giving intravenous fluids and drugs, are used to try to improve blood pressure. Provided the infection is rapidly controlled, patients will make a complete recovery.

SHINGLES
A local skin infection due to the herpes virus varicella zoster.

Single (never repeated) outbreaks of mild shingles can happen when the immune system is temporarily damped down by stress or old age. More severe or repeated attacks of shingles can be a sign of more serious immune deficiency, caused, for example, by HIV infection (p. 144) or chronic lymphocytic leukaemia (p. 148).

What are the causes?
Shingles is due to the varicella zoster virus (VZV) which causes chickenpox when it first infects people, usually in childhood. The T cells of the immune system bring the chickenpox under control after a few days, but the virus remains hidden in the nervous system.

What are the symptoms?
If the immune system is damaged, the virus breaks out again, causing a painful rash in a belt-like pattern around one side of the trunk. Sometimes shingles also affects one side of the face, when it can damage the vision.

How is it diagnosed?
Shingles may be suspected from the patient's history and the type and position of the rash. A definitive diagnosis can be reached by culturing samples of spots in a laboratory.

What are the treatment options?

Treatment with the antiviral drug aciclovir can reduce the length of a shingles attack. Painkillers are usually needed because the pain can be severe and it can persist after the rash has disappeared. Occasionally there may be permanent numbness or tingling of the skin at the site of the attack.

SICKLE CELL DISEASE

An inherited form of anaemia in which a large number of red blood cells become sickle shaped.

Sickle cell disease is most common among people of Afro-Caribbean descent and very rare in white Europeans.

What are the causes?

The disease is caused by a mutation in the haemoglobin gene. When the amount of oxygen in the blood is low, abnormal haemoglobin molecules form crystals that damage red cells, resulting in anaemia. Damaged red cells also block blood vessels, causing oxygen levels in the blood to fall even further.

The severity of the sickle syndrome depends on the number of abnormal genes. A patient with one abnormal gene (for instance, someone who has inherited a normal gene from the mother and an abnormal gene from the father) has a less severe disease called sickle cell trait. There are symptoms only when oxygen levels are low, such as when flying in unpressurised aeroplanes. People with the more severe sickle cell disease have inherited two sets of abnormal haemoglobin genes and can develop symptoms at any time. It may be that sickle cell trait is an advantage in Africa; the malaria parasite finds it much harder to infect red cells that contain this haemoglobin, so carrying one set of abnormal genes may give some protection from malaria.

What are the symptoms?

Anaemia and bone pain caused by damaged red blood cells blocking the blood vessels.

How is it diagnosed?

The abnormal haemoglobin can be detected by carrying out haemoglobin electrophoresis.

What are the treatment options?

Antibiotics to prevent infections are given. Blood transfusions may be an option, and research is on-going into stem cell and bone marrow transplant for sufferers.

AT THE LEADING EDGE

Using umbilical cord blood to treat sickle cell disease

A baby's umbilical cord is rich in stem cells, the building blocks of the immune system and whole blood. In 1998 researchers in Atlanta, USA, took blood from the cord of an unrelated baby and gave it to a 12-year-old boy with sickle cell disease. The boy had experienced his first stroke at five years old, and despite regular blood transfusions was in constant pain and at risk of a second stroke. Normal red cells were produced by stem cells in the cord blood and the boy's symptoms improved. Unlike bone marrow transplant, cord blood doesn't have to be a good match to be effective; because the cells in cord blood are immature, a host does not recognise them as foreign and reject them. The belief was that the cord blood would enable the patient to manufacture healthy blood cells.

SPLENOMEGALY

This term simply means 'big spleen' and describes the swelling of the spleen due to a range of illnesses.

The spleen is an organ about the size of a fist in the upper abdomen. One of its roles is to act as a filter: it can remove bacteria from the blood, for example. It also removes old red cells, neutrophils and platelets. If the spleen is enlarged, it may start removing healthy cells from the blood, causing red cell, platelet and neutrophil counts to fall. An enlarged spleen is also at higher risk of rupture following injury.

What are the causes?

The spleen becomes enlarged transiently in some cases of infectious mononucleosis (glandular fever), but can become more permanently enlarged in lymphoma and leukaemia, when it fills up with abnormal blood cells. In some forms of liver disease, the spleen swells because the liver increases the amount of blood flowing through it. There are several other forms of splenomegaly, including immune thrombocytopenia, ITP (p. 146).

What are the symptoms?

The prime symptom is the enlarged spleen, but general symptoms of infection such as fever may also be present.

How is it diagnosed?
Physical examination and medical history of the patient will point to a diagnosis.

What are the treatment options?
If the cause of splenomegaly cannot be treated, the spleen may need to be surgically removed.

SYSTEMIC LUPUS ERYTHEMATOSUS
An autoimmune disease in which the immune system makes antibodies against DNA.

What are the causes?
DNA can leak from damaged cells and enter the blood, where antibodies bind on it. A DNA antibody circulating in the blood triggers off damage. In systemic lupus erythematosus (SLE) the damage takes the form of inflamed blood vessels, particularly at key sites such as the skin, joints and kidneys. Because SLE causes blood vessel inflammation, it is classed as a type of vasculitis.

SLE tends to run in families. In most cases, the genetic basis for this inheritance is not known, but in some cases patients inherit a deficiency in the complement proteins. Like most autoimmune diseases, although there is a strong genetic risk of getting the disease, an environmental trigger is also required. In some women at least, this may be taking the contraceptive pill or other medications.

What are the symptoms?
SLE tends to affect young women. Initial symptoms may include rashes on parts of the skin exposed to the sun, Raynaud's phenomenon and joint pain. Like many autoimmune diseases, SLE can stay relatively mild or become more severe, in which case there can be kidney and brain damage, blood clots and miscarriages.

How is it diagnosed?
Lupus is hard to diagnose and easy to miss. Doctors need to know about all of the symptoms. A special autoantibody test (the antinuclear antibody test – 98 per cent of SLE sufferers have this antibody in their blood) is used to pinpoint a diagnosis of SLE.

What are the treatment options?
The treatment of SLE depends on the severity of each individual case. For mild cases, anti-inflammatory drugs may be enough; in more severe cases, immunosuppressive drugs may have to be given. Although most symptoms can be controlled, SLE does not go away and most patients require treatment for life.

THALASSAEMIA
An inherited condition in which mutations in the haemoglobin gene make it impossible for the body to make haemoglobin.

Thalassaemia is common in people from the Mediterranean region, Asia and some parts of Africa. It may be that, as with sickle cell trait (p. 153), having one abnormal gene offers some protection from malaria.

About 100,000 babies worldwide are born with severe forms of thalassaemia each year.

What are the causes?
The mild form of thalassaemia is caused by inheriting just one abnormal gene. In this case it is still possible for the patient to make red blood cells. People who inherit two abnormal genes have severe problems making red cells.

What are the symptoms?
People with mild forms of the disease tend to be anaemic; for people who inherit two abnormal genes, the anaemia is severe. Iron is usually incorporated with haemoglobin, but patients with severe thalassaemia cannot make haemoglobin, so iron builds up in the body, poisoning the liver. Blood tests show the presence of the condition.

What are the treatment options?
Regular blood transfusions may be necessary for more severe cases, with antibiotics to treat infection. Repeated transfusions, however, can lead to iron overload, so drugs are needed to correct this. Bone marrow transplant offers a cure, but there are few suitable donors. It is hoped that gene therapy may offer the possibility of a cure.

VASCULITIS
This term applies to a group of diseases which are caused by inflammation of the blood vessels.

What are the causes?
There are many different types of vasculitis, which are generally caused by the immune system. Each one tends to affect certain groups and produces distinct symptoms.

Sometimes inflammation of blood vessels is due to mixtures of antibody and target molecules circulating in the blood. SLE (p. 154) is an example of damage by what is referred to as immune complexes. Immune complexes can occur after sore throats caused by bacteria, when complexes of antibody and bacterial protein circulate in the blood.

In other instances, the immune system makes a direct attack on the blood vessels, as a type of autoimmunity.

Little is known about the causes of temporal arteritis, a common vasculitis affecting elderly people, which results in inflammation in the blood vessels in the head. Behçet's disease is another vasculitis, which affects people along the old Silk Route that extended from the Middle East to China. For both temporal arteritis and Behçet's disease there must be a specific causation to affect such particular groups. As with all autoimmune problems, it is likely that there is a genetic basis for these diseases, but that an environmental trigger (maybe an infection) is needed to initiate them.

What are the symptoms?
In cases of immune complexes circulating in the bloodstream, damage to the kidneys is likely. Severe headaches are the usual symptom of temporal arteritis, but blindness or stroke can sometimes develop. In Behçet's disease, ulcers form in the mouth and on the genitals, and eye disease and skin and joint problems are characteristic.

How is it diagnosed?
Vasculitis can sometimes be diagnosed on the basis of specific blood tests, for example the anti-nuclear antibody test in SLE. For other diseases, including Behçet's disease and temporal arteritis, there is no specific blood test and the diagnosis is apparent from the unusual symptoms.

What are the treatment options?
Most types of vasculitis, except those caused by infection, respond well to immunosuppressive drugs. In these cases the outlook is good.

X-LINKED DISORDERS
Genetic disorders resulting from mutations on the X chromosome.

The genetic code is contained in the 23 chromosomes present in most body cells. Each of these chromosomes is present as a pair: one inherited from the mother, the other from the father. For chromosomes 1–22, each member of

the pair looks very similar, although the detailed genetic codes are different. The 23rd chromosome determines the sex of an individual and the two members of the pair look very different. Chromosome 23 can be an X chromosome or a much smaller Y chromosome. Women have two X chromosomes; men have an X chromosome and a Y chromosome.

When eggs are made in a woman's ovaries, each egg receives just one chromosome from each pair. As women have two X chromosomes, each egg will receive one of these. Sperm cells produced by men also receive one of each pair of chromosomes. Because men's cells have an X and a Y chromosome, each sperm can be either X or Y. An egg fertilised by an X sperm will make a female (XX) baby; an egg fertilised by a Y sperm will make a male (XY) baby. Because there is a 50 per cent chance of either of these happening, about 50 per cent of babies are boys and 50 per cent are girls. Some diseases are the result of mutations on the X chromosome.

What are the causes?
Women are not usually affected by these diseases because they have two X chromosomes; even if they inherit a mutated X chromosome, this will be balanced by a normal one. Only women can carry X-linked disorders. Men have just one X chromosome, so if they inherit a mutation, it will cause disease.

What are the symptoms?
The symptoms will be particular to the disease. X-linked disorders include: chronic granulomatous disease (p. 140); some forms of SCID (p. 151); and antibody deficiency (p. 137). The best-known disease is haemophilia (p. 144), of which a famous example is the family of Queen Victoria, which shows a typical X-linked disease pattern. Victoria was a carrier of haemophilia, as were two daughters and four granddaughters. She also had one affected son, three affected grandsons and five affected great-grandsons.

How is it diagnosed?
It is now possible for genetic testing to identify a female carrier of these diseases. It is then possible to see if an unborn male fetus is affected, if the carrier wishes.

What are the treatment options?
Treatment for these X-linked conditions aims at relieving the symptoms. A patient's outlook will depend on the particular disease or disorder.

Index

Acknowledgments

Carroll & Brown Limited would also like to thank:

Picture researcher
Sandra Schneider

Production manager
Karol Davies

Production controller
Nigel Reed

Computer management
Paul Stradling

Indexer
Jill Dormon

3-D anatomy
Mirashade/Matt Gould

Illustrators
Andy Baker, Rajeev Doshi/Regraphica, Kevin Jones Associates, Mikki Rain, John Woodcock

Layout and illustration assistance
Joanna Cameron

Photographer
Jules Selmes

Photographic sources
SPL = Science Photo Library

1 SPL
6 *(right)* Getty Images
7 Michael Abbey/SPL
8 *(top left)* CNRI/SPL
8 *(background)* Andrew Syred/SPL
8/9 Getty Images
10 *(top)* Edelmann/SPL
10/11 *(background)* Andrew Syred/SPL
10/11 Dan McCoy/Rainbow/medipics
11 *(left)* Getty Images
11 *(right)* Roy Morsch/Corbis
12 *(background)* Andrew Syred/SPL
12 *(left)* LWA-Stephen Welstead/Corbis
12 *(right)* Tom & Dee McCarthy/ Corbis
13 *(top)* Hank Morgan/SPL
13 CNRI/SPL
14 *(centre)* Getty Images
(right) NIBSC/SPL
19 BSIP Meullemiestre/SPL

27 NIBSC/SPL
30 SPL
38 Getty Images
39 *(top, centre)* Getty Images
(bottom) Jose Luis Pelaez Inc/ Corbis
40 *(centre)* Getty Images
41 Getty Images
42 *(top right)* Getty Images
(4th from top) Getty Images
43 Getty Images
45 *(left)* Getty Images
47 Getty Images
51 John Henley/Corbis
54 *(left, centre, bottom)* Getty Images
55 TEK Image/SPL
58 Getty Images
59 *(top, 3rd from top)* Getty Images
62 Tiziana & Gianni Baldizzone/ Corbis
63 *(top)* Getty Images
66 *(bottom)* Getty Images
70 www.tefal.co.uk
75 *(right, 2nd, 3rd from top, bottom)* Getty Images
78 Getty Images
83 Getty Images
84 Getty Images
87 *(left)* Getty Images
87 *(top right)* Sinclair Stammers/SPL
88 Getty Images
90 Sinclair Stammers/SPL
91 London School of Hygiene and Tropical Medicine/SPL
92 Medipics
93 Getty Images
96 *(left)* Dr Gopal Murti/SPL
(centre) TEK Image/SPL
(right) Wellcome Trust Medical Photographic Library
97 Nina Lampen/SPL
100 Dr Gopal Murti/SPL
103 Wellcome Trust Medical Photographic Library
104 *(top)* Charles Gupton/Corbis
(bottom) Saturn Stills/SPL
105 John Greim/SPL
106 John Radcliffe Hospital/SPL
107 *(top)* Michael Abbey/SPL
(bottom) Geoff Tompkinson/SPL
108 Simon Fraser/Department of Haematology/RVI, Newcastle/SPL
110 TEK Image/SPL
111 Philippe Plailly/Eurelios/SPL
114 *(top)* Cordelia Molloy/SPL
(bottom) Getty Images-Foodpix
115 Jerry Mason/SPL

116 TEK Image/SPL
117 St Bartholomew's Hospital/SPL
118 Nina Lampen/SPL
119 John Greim/SPL
120 Colin Cuthbert/SPL
121 Colin Cuthbert/SPL
123 Great Ormond Street
124 *(top)* Geoff Tompkinson/SPL
(centre) SPL
(bottom) Andrew Syred/SPL
125 *(top)* Andrew Tsiaras/SPL
(bottom) Great Ormond Street
127 Bill Varie/Corbis
129 Copyright 2002, The Regents of the University of Michigan
130 Getty Images
131 Getty Images

Back cover *(centre)* Getty Images
(right) TEK Image/SPL

Contact details
NHS Direct 0845 4647
www.nhsdirect.nhs.uk

NHS Quitline 0800 002200

Terrence Higgins Trust
www.tht.org.uk
Living well with HIV phoneline
0845 947 0047

Transplant Games
www.TransWeb.org

Jeans for Genes campaign
Great Ormond Street Hospital for Children NHS Trust
Great Ormond Street
London WC1N 3JH
The Institute for Child Health
30 Guildford Street
London WC1N 1EH

Organ donation
www.nhsorgandonor.net
0845 60 60 400

Blood Transfusion Service
www.blood.co.uk
0845 7 711 711